Mills & Boon Classics

A chance to read and collect some of the best-loved novels from Mills & Boon – the world's largest publisher of romantic fiction.

Every month, four titles by favourite Mills & Boon authors will be re-published in the *Classics* series.

A list of other titles in the *Classics* series can be found at the end of this book.

Violet Winspear

RAPTURE OF THE DESERT

MILLS & BOON LIMITED
LONDON · TORONTO

All the characters in this book have no existence outside the imagination of the Author, and have no relation whatsoever to anyone bearing the same name or names. They are not even distantly inspired by any individual known or unknown to the Author, and all the incidents are pure invention.

The text of this publication or any part thereof may not be reproduced or transmitted in any form or by any means, electronic or mechanical, including photocopying, recording, storage in an information retrieval system, or otherwise, without the written permission of the publisher.

This book is sold subject to the condition that it shall not, by way of trade or otherwise, be lent, resold, hired out or otherwise circulated without the prior consent of the publisher in any form of binding or cover other than that in which it is published and without a similar condition including this condition being imposed on the subsequent purchaser.

First published 1972
Australian copyright 1980
Philippine copyright 1980
This edition 1980

© Violet Winspear 1972

ISBN 0 263 73325 4

Set in Linotype Baskerville 10/11½ pt

Made and printed in Great Britain by Richard Clay (The Chaucer Press), Ltd., Bungay, Suffolk

CHAPTER ONE

'You have my answer,' said the man who was dressed all in grey, with even a distinguished dash of it through his hair. 'A year from today and you might dance again. The fall you had from those railway steps was a serious one and you might well have been killed, or crippled for life. But luck and skill were on your side and the operation which you underwent was almost a total success. It will become a complete one, if for the next twelve months you set aside your career in ballet and turn to some less strenuous occupation.'

'A whole year!' The girl in the chair at the opposite side of Van Harrington's desk looked at him as if he pronounced for her a life sentence away from her beloved dancing. Indeed it was her life. Since the age of seven she had worked and slaved for love of the dance, and now at twenty-two she was a recognised soloist, and only a few weeks previous to her accident she had danced in Russia at the Bolshoi Theatre where the stage was so wonderfully spacious, so made for those dramatic ballets which were for her the breath of life.

'Dancing is all I know,' she said tensely.

'Unless you wish to undo all the skilful work which has made you fit again, then forget that you are a dancer, Miss Devrel. A year is not for ever.'

'You said cautiously that I *might* dance again, Mr Harrington. Your verdict doesn't sound conclusive.'

'Medical men are rather like bankers.' His smile was

brief but kind. 'We are cautious with our handouts. I have given you back a sound enough body, but you must be careful not to squander your strength. You could return to your career next week, and be again my patient in four weeks. Wait a year and we will see then——'

'But a year away from dancing could mean the end for me! Unless a ballet dancer's body is kept continually in practice there is a gradual lessening of speed and grace.' Chrys Devrel drew a sigh of near despair! 'If you say I must stop dancing, then I'm finished.'

'Nonsense!' Now he spoke sharply, as if scolding a child. 'Life has many things to offer an attractive young woman. Your heart won't easily break, but your body could be ruined for good unless you accept my advice. Well, Miss Devrel, what are you going to do?'

She avoided his stern gaze by looking down at her hands, slim and clasped together as if they sought to comfort each other. 'You don't give me much choice,' she said at last. 'I must swallow the bitter pill of a ruined career in order to keep my bodily health. I—I'm not altogether a fool, so I shall have to abide by what you say.'

'You will make me a firm promise?' He rose to his feet and came round to where she sat. Chrys stood up and she felt numb inside as he took her hands in his. 'Come now, young woman, give me your word that you will not perform a single pirouette for the next twelve months.'

'I wouldn't dare a single ballet step,' she replied. 'One alone would lead me on to dance and dance, until I dropped. That's how much I love to dance!'

'You have, perhaps, never tried to love anything else

because to dance was all-sufficing. Now you have to face an alternative. Now you have time and lei-sure——'

'No, I shall need to work,' she broke in. 'The clinic and the operation took most of my savings. I have to find a job, but heaven alone knows what I'm suited for! I dare not find work in a theatre—my will-power isn't strong enough for that.'

The surgeon gazed down at her, his look an effortless one, because she had dark gold hair framing a white, slender, purely-boned face. The small lobes of her ears were pierced by small gold rings, and her eyes were in-tensely blue. She gave an impression of being fragile, but in reality she was supple as fine silk and equally resilient.

She tilted her chin. 'Something will come along, I daresay, but I can't promise to give it my devotion or my love. Thank you again, Mr Harrington, for all your kindness.'

He walked with her to the door of his consultation room. 'Goodbye, Miss Devrel. As I said before, a year soon passes.'

'I suppose it does,' she said, but as she left him and made her way down the stairs to the front door she knew that even a week away from the *barre* could rob a dancer of some of her skill. She smiled absently at the woman who opened the door for her, and as she stepped into Wimpole Street she felt as if it might as well have been raining instead of looking so bright and cheerful. She walked to the end of the street and there she hailed a cab and asked the driver to take her to the St Clement's Hotel, where she was meeting her sister for tea.

Dove took life as it came and had never bothered about a career. Dove had wanted only to marry, and in a couple of weeks she would walk up the aisle and look glowingly expectant and content.

Chrys sat back against the leather upholstery of the cab and breathed the tang of cigar smoke left by the previous occupant. Life for her had become so tangled up since that awful moment at Fenchurch Street Station when she tripped on the steps there, while running to catch a train. She had fallen backwards, all the way down to the hard ground, crushing a couple of the fine, intricate bones in her spine. The pain had been unbelievable, and the fear of never walking again had been like a nightmare from which she had seemed not to awake for hours and days.

The cab swept through Soho, so unnaturally quiet at this time of the day, and made its way past a towered church that looked so old in the sunlight. She noted the time by the church clock and knew that Dove would already be up in the penthouse lounge, gazing dreamily from the wide windows, or studying that sweet and simple engagement ring of hers. With that unimpaired grace which had made it too easy for her to believe that she would soon be able to dance again Chrys stepped out of the cab and paid the driver. She felt his eyes on her face, but it meant little to her that like Van Harrington he found the bones, and the shape and the colour of her eyes, a pleasing blend.

She turned and walked into the hotel. She crossed the carpeted foyer to the express lifts and pressed the button of the one that would take her up to the lounge. Dove would be sympathetic, but she would be like the surgeon and say that Chrys should count her blessings.

Her health was restored and she could *walk*. Dove would smile that dove-like smile of hers and insinuate that Chrys find a beau and enjoy the pleasure of falling in love.

There was a little twist of a smile on Chrys's mouth as the lift doors opened and she stepped out and saw her sister composedly seated on a long couch by the panoramic windows, the sun on her smooth young profile.

Dove turned instinctively as if she felt the sudden tightening of the bond between them. A smile broke on her soft pink lips and she jumped to her feet. Her hair was a lighter gold than Chrys's, her eyes a gentler blue, and the curve of her chin was less obstinate. She was the pretty sister, the more popular one with the young men of Westcliff, their home town. She had not the haughty tilt to her head that made Chrys seem too distant to touch. Her lips were not those of a passionate and talented spirit.

She was like her name, a dove, and Chrys loved her, but could never be half so sweet, or ready for the tender delights of love with a young executive who, quite literally, adored his bride-to-be.

The sisters embraced, and then a waiter came to take their order. 'Tea and cream cakes,' said Dove, who in a couple of years would be plump and quite unconcerned.

'Well, darling?' She studied her sister's composed but very white face with concerned eyes. 'What was the great man's verdict?'

'I must give up dancing for a year, or find myself flat on my back again.' Chrys spoke through forcibly controlled lips.

'Well, that isn't too bad.' Dove squeezed her hand. 'A year will soon go by and then you can start again, if that's what you truly want.'

'I can think of nothing else to want.' A thread of emotion broke through the control of Chrys's voice. Dove had never really understood her temperament; her need to find poetry and passion through the medium of the dance. Dove could only see life through the eyes of an average young woman seeking security and protection by marrying a nice, steady, loving man. Dove was not—artistic.

Chrys sighed and gazed from the windows at the panorama of London. Somewhere in that teeming city she must find another occupation and hope it would keep her busy enough, and at the end of the day tired enough not to pine after the ballet company and the people she was so in tune with. God, but it would be awful not to be among her own sort, living a life that was never dull or humdrum. There was magic in the air breathed by those connected with ballet. There was beauty of movement, and the drama of temperament.

'Heaven knows what I shall find to do!' Her blue eyes burned with resentment and unshed tears, but unlike Dove she never found it easy to relieve her feelings by weeping. She was much more inclined to give way to temper.

The waiter arrived with a tray on which stood tea things and a plate of delectable pastries. He arranged the pot and cups on the table in front of them and withdrew.

'Shall I be mother?' Dove giggled a little, for it was an open secret that she planned to start a family as soon as she was married to Jeremy.

'Yes, do enjoy yourself and get in some practice,' said Chrys, a trifle scornfully. 'Honestly, Dove, have you never wanted to do something exciting with your life?'

'I consider marriage a very exciting thing.' Dove poured the tea, and with a smile of anticipation she selected a cream and honey slice, almost purring with pleasure. 'One of these days, Chrys, you're going to fall in love with a bump, and it will so shake you that you won't know whether you're on your head or your heels. I hope I'm around to see it happen.'

Chrys stirred her tea moodily. 'I just love to dance, and can't believe that any man could offer me the delight I feel when I spin across a stage and stretch my body to the very limits of its endurance.'

'Heavens, it sounds such hard work.' Dove forked pastry into her pink mouth. 'I've never known you to relax, Chrys. In fact the only time I've ever seen you flat on your back was during those weeks you spent in hospital. D'you remember what Nan used to call us when we were kids? The Persian tabby, and the sleek alley cat! She wasn't far wrong, was she? I like comfort and being pampered. But you like to go prowling among the arty types of London, alert and sleek as any alley cat, but without the amoral temperament. Have you never been attracted to a man?'

Chrys reviewed in her mind the various men she had met during the course of her career. Some she had admired for their artistic abilities but she couldn't remember losing a heartbeat over a single one of them. 'Perhaps I'm frigid,' she said, with a cynical smile. 'Well, Dove, have you any ideas about what I should do while my career goes to pot in the coming year?'

'Don't say it like that, Chrys! As if your life is half

over.' Dove stopped eating pastry like a gourmand and regarded her sister with fond, and faintly, anxious eyes. 'Look, darling, there is a job you can tackle if only you'll shake off your moodiness and try to be interested in other things beside Swan Lake and being the Pavlova of the Seventies. I wouldn't mention it before you saw Van Harrington and heard what he had to say about your future——'

'A job?' Chrys broke in. 'Not in that darned office of Jerry's?'

'Don't call him Jerry,' Dove pleaded. 'It makes me think of that strip cartoon, the one about the cat and the mouse. No, pet, this has to do with Jeremy's aunt, the one who travels a lot, and who used to go on "digs" with her husband. It's a sort of mania with her. France one month, Scotland the next, and like as not Romania for good measure! Well, my darling spouse-to-be was telling me that she's been left in the lurch by her travelling companion, a mousy little woman who suddenly ran off with an American bartender in Paris. Jeremy said his Aunt Kate was livid. She has this journey all fixed up for the East, and can't seem to find the right person to keep her company—Chrys, the job would be better for you than some nine-to-five office routine. You'd be bound to hate that.'

'And prefer being companion to some bossy globe-trotting woman?' It seemed so mid-Victorian, so absurd a role for her, that Chrys had to laugh. 'Not on your life, dear sister! I'm not cut out for dabbing *eau de cologne* on an elderly brow, and reading the saga of Barchester while the train speeds through some uncomfortable Eastern landscape. I'd hate trotting round bazaars, being mousy and obedient.'

'But I don't think Aunt Kate is like that at all,' Dove objected. 'Jeremy says she's his favourite aunt and quite a worldly sort of woman. She once wrote a thriller about the tomb of that Egyptian boy king— king of the moon, wasn't he? It was a best-seller, I believe. And she knows lots of interesting people, and helped to get refugees out of Cambodia not so long ago. You'd be bound to like her.'

'H'm.' Chrys sat thoughtful, her face at its most pensive and therefore its most beautiful; the classic, half-enchanted face of the ballerina. 'I couldn't stand a fluffy type of employer, or a butch with bobbed hair. We once had a choreographer like that, and she came to my dressing-room one rehearsal morning and made a pass at me.'

'No!' Dove's eyes widened to such an extent that they threatened to fall out. 'Whatever did you do?'

'Told her frankly that because I wasn't sleeping around with men that didn't mean I preferred the company of a woman. She hated me after that. Those sort of women harbour grudges, unlike men who take a slap if they make an unwanted pass and then shrug it off.'

'I'd be terrified of the people you've known, Chrys.' Dove gave a little shiver. 'Why don't you find a nice young man and do what I'm doing? Marriage isn't so bad.'

'It's a tie.' Chrys poured herself some more tea and added milk but no sugar. Instinctively she was still looking after her svelte dancing figure. 'And meeting all sorts of people is all part of living. 'I'd sooner have my eyes open than closed to the oddities of life.'

'Yet,' murmured Dove, 'you look so unworldly. A

13

little like Undine when you dance the part. Part enchanted. In some ways I believe you shrink from love because it means sharing yourself with another person.'

'Yes, perhaps,' said Chrys. 'Men can be terribly demanding. Even your Jeremy will expect you to live for him. He'll often take you for granted, but heaven help you if you ever show him a moment's disinterest. He'll go out on a binge, or find himself a blonde to flirt with.'

'Don't you mean a brunette?' Dove smiled and touched her fair hair with her ringed hand, very much in love and incapable of finding Jeremy anything but a perfect and adoring male. It was at that moment, as the sunlight slanted through the large windows and touched the faces and the hair of the Devrel sisters, that both of them became conscious of a pair of eyes upon them.

So direct a gaze that it had to be felt, and when met, unavoided.

It was Dove, whose interest in men was more personal than her sister's, who glanced across the lounge and caught her breath so hard that Chrys was obliged to look as well.

He sat alone smoking a cigar, and the very perfection of the dark grey suit he wore made him seem illimitably foreign. His eyes dwelt on her face with not a flicker of the dark lashes, and there was something so long and lean and inimitably graceful about his body that Chrys thought at once that he must be a perfect dancer. Her gaze sped to his feet in hand-tailored shoes; long narrow feet to match the hand holding the dark cigar.

Then again his eyes were looking directly into hers

14

and a strange shudder had swept through her before she even realised that a stranger could invade her being with his eyes alone.

She looked quickly away from him, hating herself for a coward, but aware that she had just met the eyes of a man who knew women as an English stockbroker knew the pound note!

'Chrys, you're blushing!' There was an exultant note in Dove's voice, albeit she whispered, as if the lone male might have ears as penetrating as his eyes. 'Isn't he something! And fancy seeing him here at the St Clement's.'

'Who the devil is he, then?' Chrys felt annoyed with herself for letting the glance of a mere male shake her. 'He's too abominably good-looking to be respectable, that's for sure!'

'Darling, do mind your voice,' Dove hissed. 'I saw his picture in the *Daily Post* yesterday. They say he only cares about horses, cards, and fine living. He travels all over the world, so he must be very well off.'

'No doubt he's a card-sharp,' Chrys rejoined. 'With those eyes he can probably strip the cards to their last diamond.'

'But I don't think he's one of those——' Dove cast him a hasty glance, and at once he inclined his head, with its thick hair like smoked silver, and a quiver of amusement ran round the bold line of his lips.

'Oh!' It was Dove's turn to blush. 'Oh, I do see what you mean, Chrys!'

'Humph, I'm glad you're not that innocent, for Jeremy's sake!' Chrys spoke tartly. 'The damned decadent Adonis is looking right at us. He knows full well we're talking about him ... who is he, Dove?'

'Well, as I said, it isn't right for you to call him a card-sharp.' Dove was now so nervous that she was tearing a paper napkin to shreds. 'He's Prince Anton de Casenove, and I really don't know whether to be thrilled or frightened that he bowed to me. He has Russian royal blood in him, and they say he attracts women like a magnet. Oh, heavens, even I can feel the pull of him, and I'm engaged to Jeremy!'

'Don't let it upset you, pet,' Chrys said drily. 'Both the devil and the divine have this pull on the female of the species. I'm sure if *milor* suddenly rose to his feet and came over here to kiss your hand, you would run like a pretty hare.'

'And what would you do?' Dove spoke huffily. 'Slap his face?'

'I might,' Chrys drawled. 'I'd hate to be kissed by a man with his kind of face. I can't make up my mind whether he's wickedly good-looking, or gaunt and interesting. I'm sure all that suavity is only a thin veneer over a basic savage.'

'Chrys, that's putting it a bit strongly.' But Dove giggled, as if it excited her own basic niceness and timidity that a wicked-looking prince should bow to her. 'I wonder why he's all alone? D'you suppose he's waiting for a woman?'

'No.' Chrys was amazed that she felt so sure. 'He's the type that keeps women waiting. I believe he's sitting there with the deliberate intention of putting the pair of us into a flap. He's hoping we'll either make a bolt for the lift, or one of us will give him the eye in the hope that he'll come over here. I bet if I gave him the eye right now, he'd shrivel me with a frosty look and enjoy doing it. That one believes in the *harem*,

16

not in the liberation of feminine libido.'

'Would you dare?' Dove spoke so excitedly that she forgot to whisper.

Immediately, from the corner of her eye, Chrys saw that dark cigar make a downward stab into the ashtray. That devil was waiting for her to dare something. Being a foreigner he obviously believed that European women were fast, and he was waiting for her to prove him right.

As if nerving herself for that moment when a dancer runs from the wings into the many eyes of the stage lights, beyond which are the thousand human eyes of her audience, Chrys slowly turned her head so that she was looking directly at Prince Anton de Casenove. He was looking at her and there was challenge in every graceful line of him; in the way he held his haughty head and revealed his eyes by the sudden rapid lifting of his lashes.

Deep grey, almost smoky eyes ... shockingly beautiful eyes!

Never as a dancer had she been a victim of stage fright ... but now fright took hold of her and she was the one who felt like bolting like a hare for the express lift. There was something about those eyes that stripped her of all her assurance and made her feel that she was a girl of sixteen again, who had never been out of England, and never been kissed.

With a sense of total surprise she realised that it was true about the kissing part ... only male dancers had ever set their lips to hers, and only because it was all part of the ballet ... Albrecht with Giselle and nothing more.

'I think we'd better be going, Dove.' She looked

round for the waiter and quickly beckoned him over. Dove was looking a little let down.

'Scared of him?' she asked.

'No, but it suddenly seemed a foolish game, like a pair of schoolgirls imagining that a grown man would be interested in their nonsense. I'll pay the bill and we can be off.'

Chrys avoided her sister's stare as she settled up with the waiter and pulled on her gloves. They walked across to the lift, and she knew he was still there on the black leather seat, perfectly at his ease, and perfectly aware that she was running away. She was glad when the lift door closed and she could feel the steel enclosure swooping herself and Dove to the ground floor. They stepped out and made for the swing doors leading on to the street.

They were outside and she was about to hail a cab when Dove clutched at her arm. 'My parcel,' she wailed. 'My wedding shoes! I collected them just before we met for tea, and I've gone and left them up in the lounge. Oh, Chrys!' Dove glanced wildly at her wristwatch. 'I'm meeting Jeremy and we're driving over to Hampstead to see his mother. I daren't be late. Jeremy's an angel, but Mrs Stanton is a bit of a tartar. Look, can you go back for my shoes? I must grab that taxi and be off!'

'You are the limit, Dove.' Chrys gave a rueful laugh. 'You're so cockeyed about that young man that you'll lose your head before the great day arrives. Run, then, or that cab will be snapped up. The busy hour is just starting.'

'Angel! I'll see you later on. The shoe box is a pink one in a Fereaux bag. See you!' Dove darted to the

18

cab and climbed in, and the next moment it was gone and Chrys was standing alone on the pavement. It was now past five, and the shadows of the church across the road, and the buildings round about had a smear to them, they were stretching as the sun slid down the sky, going pink and unreal. Chrys tilted her chin and walked back into the hotel.

Once again she rode up swiftly to the lounge, its fittings and its carpet bathed in a pink glow as she walked across to the seat where she had taken tea with Dove. She didn't look left or right, but just kept on going . . . only to find the parcel gone!

Now she had to look around for the waiter, only to find the lounge deserted but for a tall, tall figure who was coming inexorably towards her. On his feet he was even more elegant, with that silent way of walking which she had felt was the requisite of Russian male dancers, as if the soles of their feet were padded with velvet, and springy as the paws of the leopard.

She stood very still, a tall girl herself, with coiled gold hair, pure pale features, and eyes spooned out of a pure blue sky. Her suit of tawny wool fitted her without a wrinkle, for she had learned long ago the ballet dancer's art of always looking neat. She was silent and still and strangely trapped, high above London, it seemed, with a man in whom she had detected a savage flame, uncooled by civilised living, and the sartorial elegance of the man of the world.

'Your pardon, *madame*, but can I be of service? You appear to have lost something?'

'A parcel.' The words seemed to scrape her dry throat. 'A pair of wedding shoes which were in a paper bag on this seat.'

'Shoes for a wedding, eh?' He slowly raised a black brow. 'I expect the waiter has carried them away, and if we ask at the desk they may be there awaiting collection. Shall we see?'

'I don't wish to bother you.'

'It would only bother me if I could not help a bride-to-be to find her wedding slippers. Come, let us ask, and do stop looking so anxious. Are they golden slippers?' He smiled briefly as he spoke and then gestured her to walk ahead of him among the low tables to the aisle leading to the porter's desk facing the row of express lifts. She obeyed him, and felt him close behind her, head and shoulders above her, lean and lethal as one of those fine and glittering swords which she had seen in a museum in Moscow ... the type that officers of the Czarina's guard had worn long ago with their handsome uniforms that fitted them like a glove, from their wide shoulders down over the lean hips and the long supple legs.

She almost cried out when lean fingers gripped her elbow and brought her to a standstill in front of the porter's desk. 'The young lady wishes to know if a parcel was found on that long seat over by the windows?' he said, and his English seemed extra striking because of his accent, tinging the words with a sort of mystery, as the golden arc of the falling sun was misted at its edges with exotic colour.

'Would this be the young lady's property, sir?' The porter took something from a shelf under his desk and transferred it to the counter. A decorative paper bag containing Dove's precious shoes. Chrys had noticed that Prince Anton had referred to *her* as the bride-to-be, but she didn't intend to correct him.

'Oh, good!' She spoke with all the intensity of relief which would have been Dove's and accepted the package from the porter, while the man at her side handed him a generous tip.

'Thank *you*, sir.'

'We cannot have the young lady walking barefoot up the aisle, can we?' The prince looked at Chrys as he spoke, and once again she was made aware of how amazingly beautiful were his eyes, and utterly male in their regard despite the length of his lashes and the shadows they threw on to the high-boned contours of his face.

'And now may I escort you to the ground floor?' he asked.

'I don't want to drag you away.' Her fingers clenched the handle of the shoe bag. 'I really can manage to press the button that will transfer me and my shoes to the street. Thank you——'

'I am going down myself, so we might as well go together. Come!'

It was impossible not to go with him, and as the lift door opened and she stepped past him into the enclosure, she felt again the height of him, and the darkness, and all the exotic differences deep within his bones. The door slid shut and they were alone together ... alone for the few moments it would take for the lift to reach the level of the ground. She felt strangely tense, and wondered what Dove would say if she could see her alone like this with the man whom she had called dangerous.

Suddenly there was a jarring sensation, taking her so much by surprise that she was thrown against him and aware in an instant of the muscular control and resilience of his body ... so like that of a male dancer, and yet so unalike, for the face that looked directly down at her was not a mask painted on but a detailed, utterly masculine, aware and dangerous face.

'What's happened?' She retreated away from him, to the steel wall of the lift cage.

He pressed buttons, thumped the door, but there was no response. All was still and silent as he turned to look at Chrys. Then he pronounced the alarming words. 'We appear to have come to a halt midway between the floors. Something has evidently gone wrong with the mechanism, so I had better put my finger on the alarm button, eh?'

'Right away,' she said, and her eyes were immense in her face as they dwelt on him and watched his long, lean finger stabbing the button that would set ringing the alarm bell on the ground floor. 'Oh, what a nuisance! What a thing to happen!'

'You are in a hurry, perhaps?' His eyes dwelt with total composure on the shoe bag. 'You are meeting— someone?'

'Yes,' she lied, when in truth she was going home to the flat she shared with Dove to cook herself a steak and to watch a television play, and maybe come to terms with the halt in her dancing career. 'Yes, I have a date.'

'Then let us hope that the engineers will not be too long in freeing us from our predicament.' He lounged against the steel wall, and the overhead light gleamed on his thick, well-groomed hair. 'It was your sister, of course, with whom you were taking tea? She is very pretty.'

'Thank you.' Oh lord, she thought, it was a devil of a

thing to happen, as if his dark magnetism had caused the lift to stop like this between floors. She wished he would stop looking at her, as if he knew her thoughts and was deeply amused by them. Where did she look to escape his eyes? At the roof of the lift? At the floor? At his perfect tie against the pale grey silk of his shirt?

'Tell me,' he drawled, 'if you are to wear the bride shoes, why is your sister the one who wears the engagement ring?'

'What?' Chrys stared at him, and felt so trapped.

'I had a Cossack grandmother and she handed on to me her keen eyesight.' His smile was infinitely mocking. 'I noticed while you drank tea and your sister ate cream cakes that your hands were ringless and hers bore a ring. The shoes are hers, are they not?'

'Yes—so what?' Chrys gave him a defiant and slightly annoyed look. 'She's always forgetting things.'

'But why did you return for them?' he asked, and his eyes suddenly held hers so that she couldn't look away. 'Did you wish to see me again?'

'Really!' Chrys felt quite staggered by the suggestion. 'You must have a pound on yourself if you think I came back for the shoes because I couldn't resist another look at your face. Dove had to meet her fiancé, so I—really, I'll be darned if I need to explain my actions to you. I couldn't care less about men!'

'Oh?' He arched an eyebrow in that infuriating mannerism he had, as if he rarely believed a word spoken by women. 'Are you frigid, then?'

'You,' she gasped, 'live up to the way you look!'

'And may I know how I look in your eyes, *matushka*?'

'I'm not a child,' she retorted.

'You speak like one if you say you don't care for men.

23

The woman who says that cannot care much for life.'

'Really?' she said again. 'Are women the great barren *steppes* until a wonderful man deigns to notice their existence?'

'Why not? Can a garden grow by itself? I think not, unless you like a garden of stones.'

'My likes and dislikes have nothing to do with you, *milor*.' She said it sarcastically. 'I shall be glad when they get this lift working again. It would have to happen——'

'You could have been alone,' he cut in, 'and that would have been even more alarming. As it is we can talk and pass the time. Won't you tell me your name?'

She sighed and listened for the reassuring sound of the lift's mechanism at work again, but all was still, all was silent, except for the quick beating of her heart.

CHAPTER TWO

'My name is Chrys Devrel,' she said, above the beating of her heart.

'And mine is Anton de Casenove.' He bent his head and clicked his heels, and all the time his eyes studied her face. 'You have a boy's name,' he added drily.

'I do not.' Temper sparked in her blue eyes. 'You have heard of the chrysanthemum, haven't you? If my mother had had her way I should have gone through life with that label attached to me.'

'I see.' A smile glinted deep in his smoky eyes. 'So you are the golden flower, eh?'

24

'Don't mock everything I say.' Her fingers tingled and she thought of Dove's remark about slapping his face. How easy to just lift her hand and accomplish the deed ... if only she didn't feel so sure that his retaliation would be of a kind also inherited from his Cossack grandmother.

'I don't mock you,' he rejoined. 'I find the name most suitable for someone so lissom and golden.'

The words struck her speechless and she knew that if the lift door had opened in that moment she would have fled from him like a young hare and not stopped running until she arrived at the safety of the flat, where she could shut out the world and the dangerous face of this foreign prince. But the lift door did not open, and even as she wondered how effective her fingernails would be if she had to defend herself, he made a soft growling sound in his throat that was, presumably, his way of laughing.

'How could I know that when I awoke this morning in London I would find myself tonight trapped with a girl halfway between the sky and the earth? It is quite a situation, eh? The story is bound to get into the newspapers and you may find yourself—compromised.'

'In this day and age?' she scoffed. 'Virtue no longer has that kind of value.'

'Not even to yourself?' He spoke in a dangerously soft voice. 'You think you would enjoy the notoriety of being a girl who spent hours alone in a lift with Anton de Casenove?'

'Are you so notorious?' She made herself speak lightly, but inwardly her heart flamed with a certain fear, and a touch of resentment, for she had always prided herself on being a girl who had made her way in

the dancing profession without relying on the patron-
age of a man; whose talent and dedication had been
enough to lift her out of the *corps de ballet* into the
realms of solo dancing. Not once had she needed to use
feminine wiles in order to advance her career.

It had always pleased her that she could go home to
Westcliff and remain the nice girl her parents were so
proud of. A *risqué* story in the newspapers would upset
them, and she reached out nervously to press the buttons again, but nothing happened. The lift stayed
static, and only her heart sank a little lower.

'Well, are you so terrible?' she demanded. 'Can't you
be seen with a girl without causing people to talk
about her?'

'No,' he drawled, 'not since an irate Frenchman
put a bullet through me when he caught me on the
balcony of his sister's bedroom. It was a story that
made all the newspapers, mainly because I survived the
injury. The bullet passed through my heart.'

'Your heart?' she exclaimed.

'Yes.' He smiled in an infinitely sardonic way, as if
really he was more angry than amused. 'It is a good
thing you have a sister and not a brother, eh?'

'I—I might have a boy-friend,' she fenced.

'You?' His eyes moved slowly and deliberately over
every inch of her face. 'You told me a while ago that
you didn't care for men, which is hardly the remark of
a young woman in love. Tell me, Miss Devrel, do you
ever make a bet?'

'Do you mean—gamble?'

'Yes.' He inclined his head. 'Just to pass the time
shall we make a bet? It should be amusing if nothing
else.'

26

'And what do we gamble on?'

'Ourselves. If this lift is enabled to move within the next hour, then you and I will shake hands and part. But if the lift keeps us trapped until midnight, then you give me a promise that you will dine with me tomorrow night.'

'Oh, I don't think that would be very wise.'

'Do you always allow wisdom to be your guide, Miss Devrel?'

'I have found that it pays better dividends in the end, especially for a single girl with a career she cares about.'

'Ah, so you have a career?' His eyes flickered over her, taking in the slenderness of her body, and her slim legs with the pronounced arch to her feet in the soft leather court shoes that were her one outstanding extravagance because they were hand-made. Her first *maître de ballet*, the famous Maxim di Corte, had drilled into her the good sense of always caring for her ankles and her feet. His own wife, the enchanting Lauri di Corte, never danced unless Maxim had made her slippers as supple as possible with his own hands.

Chrys smiled a little to herself as she recalled that dancing season in Venice ... the di Corte marriage worked, in her estimation, because the couple were both involved in the art of ballet. Unless a dancer found such a man, she did better to remain single.

'You smile as if you care greatly for your career.'

She came out of her reverie and glanced up at the proud, slightly melancholy face, into those eyes that glinted like magnets and seemed intent on divining her thoughts. 'It has been my life,' she said simply. 'You see, *milor*, I am a dancer.'

27

'I know.' He said it so casually. 'I saw you dance in Russia about ten months ago.'

She was so staggered by this revelation that she leaned back against the wall as if for support. 'So that was why——'

'Yes.' A lazy smile gleamed in his eyes. 'I was guilty of staring at you while you took tea with your pretty sister. I recognised you, of course. You have unusually shaded gold hair, almost tawny, like a sand cat.'

'Thank you,' she laughed a little ironically. 'It's the first time I've been likened to one of those.'

'They are elusive, graceful creatures, yet capable of tearing out a man's eyes.'

'Thank you again, Prince de Casenove.' But this time there was a thoughtful note threading her laughter. 'It's funny, but my grandmother used to refer to Dove and myself as the Persian tabby and the alley cat.'

'Ah, but that description of you is not apt.' He spoke crisply. 'You must see the sand cat with its jewel-like eyes, and its stealth when men are about, to appreciate my simile.'

'I doubt if I shall ever see one, unless the zoo has some on show.' The smile faded completely from her eyes. 'I mustn't dance for a year, so if the Company should go on tour to the Middle East I shall be left in England to pine.'

'May one ask——?'

'I had an accident a few months ago. I fell down some steps, and now I am ordered not to perform a single pirouette for a whole, long, empty year.'

'Poor *matushka*.' He seemed to mean it, but she didn't dare to look to see if that eyebrow was arched in irony. To a man such as he, who divided his time be-

28

tween French girls guarded by quick-tempered brothers, and the best stable horses, it could hardly seem of significance that her life felt empty because she was unable to carry on with the work she adored.

He was just a playboy prince ... he wouldn't understand.

'You will abide by the advice of your physician?' he said.

'I suppose I must.' She gave a little resigned shrug. '"Rather a peppercorn today than a basket of pumpkins tomorrow", as they say in the country.'

'Strange is destiny.' And then it was his turn to shrug. 'And now to revert to this little game of chance which I suggested. Will you dine with me if we are trapped in here a sufficient time for it to create an item of news in the papers? If we are seen together, let us say at the svelte Adonis Club, it will be assumed that we were acquainted when we stepped together into this lift. But if we part after the intimacy of being alone like this, with no means of escape, there will be speculation of a snide sort.'

'On account of your reputation as a rake?' she said frankly.

This time his eyebrow drastically quirked. 'The British are so blunt!'

'True,' she agreed. 'We don't wrap our proverbs in silk.'

'Such a pity,' he said drily. 'So, do you wish these newsmen to wonder how we passed the time in such close proximity?'

'We can always tell them we played Russian roulette.'

'Perhaps in a way we do play it,' he drawled. 'Whenever a man and a woman are alone there is a feeling in the air of a silent dicing with danger. Only between a man and a woman can there exist this awareness of a thousand subtle differences, each capable of arousing a thousand subtle sensations.'

A small, tense silence followed his words, and a thousand crazy thoughts rushed through Chrys's mind as her eyes skimmed the face and frame of her close companion. Beneath that impeccable shirtfront there lay a hard chest scarred by the bullet of an irate brother whose sister had succumbed to the dark, courtly, demonic attraction of this foreign prince, with Cossack instincts smouldering in his eyes, and there in the sculpture of his cheekbones and his lips.

She prayed silently and swiftly for the engineers to hurry and get this lift moving again. She strained her ears and it seemed that far below them some kind of activity could be faintly heard, but there was no vibration in the steel enclosure itself, suspended in the frame of the hotel, in which the guests would be buzzing with the news that Prince Anton de Casenove was trapped with a young woman ... the porter at that desk upstairs would know this, and by now the information would be all over the building and someone would have been bound to notify those daily devouring hawks of a spicy bit of news.

'Are you afraid to accept my bet, in case you have to pay the price?' the prince murmured. Very deliberately he glanced at his wristwatch. 'We have now been entombed for over an hour, and I have heard that when these express lifts go wrong it can be hours before they are set in motion again. We may have to spend the night together.'

'I'm shivering in my shoes,' she said flippantly.

'You may indeed do so, Miss Devrel, as the hours pass and it grows rather cold. I expect the fault in the mechanism will effect the heating of the lift as well. That is the trouble with modern amenities, they rely on the machine rather than on the man, and machines are quite careless about the feelings of a hungry, cold couple, almost strangers to each other, and locked together as if in space, while the world continues to vibrate around them. The situation is piquant, no?'

'Something terribly funny for you to relate at the card table next time you play, *milor*. I expect you will add a little relish to the tale, or will it be taken for granted that you seduced me?'

'Are you wondering if I will do so?' That black eyebrow mockingly etched itself against the pale bronze of his brow. 'According to Freud, women of virtue are more curious than their more voluptuous sisters, and the victims of their own imaginations. What makes you think that I could be bothered to try and charm a Miss Fire and Ice? Neither element is all that comfortable, especially to a man who was anticipating a choice meal, perfectly served, within the historic Regency walls of the Ritz restaurant. By contrast a tussle with a reluctant virgin strikes me like snow across my face from the very *steppes* themselves, stinging like fire and ice.'

'I'm sure,' she flashed, 'that you're accustomed to the type who fall at your feet like *harem* slaves, hair unbound and eyes pleading for the thousand delights of the Khama Sutra!'

Silence followed this little flash, fraught with a tension that broke in soft, indescribably amused laughter

31

from his lips. 'I wonder what I have done to deserve such a little spitfire for a companion in an air-locked lift? Perhaps I am being punished for my past sins, eh?'

'Well, I don't see why I should be punished with you,' she retorted.

'Why, has your life been blameless, Miss Devrel?'

'I've worked too hard to have had much time for playing around, Prince de Casenove.'

'Such a pity, *matushka*. A little play does no harm, but now you tell me that you are forced to give up your career for a while.'

'A year!' She said it bitterly, as if it were a lifetime. 'Everything was going as I planned, and then at Easter I was rushing to catch a train home for the weekend when my foot turned and I—I fell down all those steps.' Her young mouth brooded and the fire and ice of temper and misery shimmered together in her blue eyes. 'I daren't go against the surgeon's decision. I don't want to spend years on my back for the sake of yearning to dance—oh, life is so complicated at times!'

'Like the machinery of a lift,' he drawled, 'or the machinations of fate herself. Destiny is a woman, say the Arabs, and so she is perverse. What will you do with your life for a year?'

'Work in an office, I expect. Or become companion to some dotty travelling aunt of my sister's fiancé.'

'And you relish neither of these as a means of toeing the line, let us say, until you can rise again upon your toes?'

'Hardly! A whole year away from the *barre* and the stage could ruin my line, my strength of leg, my entire future as a soloist. I might have to start again at the foot of the ladder.'

'And that could be very frustrating,' he agreed.

She looked quickly at his face, and felt rather shaken by his understanding of her predicament. Her eyes questioned him, and with that courtly inclination of his head he enlightened her:

'My grandmother was known as Miroslava—which means beauty. You may not have heard of her, but a Russian prince saw her dancing in a Cossack village on the steppes and she so entranced him that he took her to the city to be trained as a dancer in ballet at the Maryinsky Theatre, which was very famous in those days. She became a great favourite there until the prince, my grandfather, married her in secret. You may not know that in Czarist days a man with noble blood in his veins was strictly forbidden to marry a commoner, so Miroslava and he had to pretend to be only lovers. Then came the uprising, and because she was known to have associated with a prince, Miroslava had to flee from Russia. My grandfather, an imperial officer in the Czarina's guard, was killed in the fighting.

'Miroslava and her servant eventually reached a strange haven, a desert province called El Kezar, where they stayed and came under the protection of a true Sheik of the desert, who always treated her son by a Russian prince as his son ... my father, of course.'

'Your father was born there, in the desert?' Chrys was interested despite her inward determination to stay aloof from this man.

'Not exactly on the tawny sands,' he drawled, 'but in a desert house given to Miroslava by the Sheik. I believe he wished to make her his wife, but she could not forget the prince. He was her one and only love.'

'It all sounds very romantic,' said Chrys. 'But you don't appear to be so singlehearted.'

He gave a soft laugh. 'Others might jump to that

33

conclusion.' He gestured at the shoe bag in her hand, with silver wedding bells printed all over it.

She had to smile herself. 'Oh dear!' she said.

'You are thinking that the reporters will take me for the prospective bridegroom?'

'There is a chance of it, knowing how quickly they will leap to conclusions in order to fill the daily papers.'

'Indeed I do know! And you think it would discompose me to be thought a man who has been trapped at last by the wiles of a woman, eh?'

'Won't it, *milor*?'

'In the circumstances it might not be such a bad thing if we are thought to be on—intimate terms.' He pinned her gaze with his and would not allow her to glance away from him. 'In this modern age what a man does with his "girl-friend" is not a subject for much speculation. But if the young woman is a stranger to him—*comprenez-vous*?'

Only too well, she nearly retorted. She would have to be caught in a lift with a man who imposed on her such an awareness of him. Had he been an Englishman, they might well have stood here, in polite silence, until the lift was put into action again. But Anton de Casenove was everything an Englishman was not! He was far too aware of the fact that she was a female, and that in itself was disconcerting. He was too dark-browed, too mocking and worldly to be acceptable as a companion in adversity.

He was altogether too aware of how her mind was working, and the sort of thoughts his near presence was engendering.

'Will it be so hard to endure if you are taken for my

bride-to-be?' he asked, in an amused tone which at the same time held a hint of menace.

'It's in my disposition to dislike being mistaken for any man's bride-to-be,' she replied, and though she spoke coolly she knew that a slight panic stirred in her eyes as they ran over his crisp dark hair, strong slanting cheekbones, and bold mouth with its shades of perpetual mockery. He looked as though he might make a ruthless lover ... a man who made his own rules and lived by them.

'You have never played the game of love, with its gambits and its thrills ... its height and its pitfalls?' He drawled the words, but his eyes were intent on her face.

'I prefer to be my own person,' she said icily. 'Love is depending on someone else for happiness.'

'And you regard that as a precarious state of living?'

'I'm afraid I do.'

'Perhaps you are a little too afraid of certain aspects of life?'

'Meaning that I'm a shrinking violet from the facts of living?' Her eyes flashed an indignant warning at him. 'I hope you don't see this situation as an opportunity to put me wise!'

'You prefer to remain innocent, eh?'

'Independent is the correct word, *milor*.'

'And you imagine that by remaining independent you can stay isolated from the emotions which are as much a part of a woman as her eyes and her hair. You may be able to control your hair, and even to keep your eyes from revealing all your thoughts, but are you so sure you have your emotions tamed?'

'They have not yet overruled me. A dancer is like a

soldier, *milor*, discipline is her second name.'

'You are still a woman,' he said suavely. 'And still a very young one, and life is always waiting to surprise us. Did you imagine when you came to take tea at the hotel that you would step into a lift and suddenly find it beyond your control to make it move? There are certain events in our lives over which we have no control at all. Destiny weaves a strange and varied pattern, not an orderly one.'

It was true, of course. Something she couldn't argue with, but none the less frustrating.

'Are you a fatalist?' she asked him.

As he considered her question he let his gaze rove the steel-lined walls of their prison. 'I believe I am,' he said. 'Usually when I am in London I stay at the Savoy, but this time I felt like a change, so I accepted the recommendation of a friend to stay at the St Clement's. We might never have met had I gone to my regular hotel.'

'I'm sure I would have survived such a loss to my education,' she rejoined.

'You are very much on the defensive,' he said, 'and I saw you shiver just then. Are you beginning to feel cold?'

'I'm perfectly all right——'

'No, you are very much on edge. You know, as I know, that if we are forced to spend the night alone like this, it will be assumed that you spent the night in my arms. Your tawny gold hair is truly remarkable—unbound it should reach to your waist.'

'I'm not about to demonstrate!' Quickly and protectively Chrys lifted a hand to the braided chignon at the nape of her slim white neck. Her hair was uncut because some of her dancing roles called for long hair and she disliked wearing false pieces which might detach themselves during a strenuous *pas de deux* with a male partner. When released from the chignon her hair reached past her lowest rib, thick and fair, and a feature of her person of which she was admittedly rather proud.

The colour came into her cheeks that this man— literally a stranger to her—should almost threaten to unloosen her hair and make it look as if he had made love to her!

'I wonder,' she said scornfully, 'if it has ever occurred to a single man on this earth that there are women who can endure to go through life without panting to be kissed and mauled?'

'Mauled, Miss Devrel?' His eyes narrowed until their greyness was lost in the shadow of his lashes. 'Is that how you regard lovemaking, as an undignified wrestling match, with the loser locked in a painful hold?'

'Isn't it exactly like that?' She stood very straight against the wall of the lift, and avoided his worldly, beautiful, wicked grey eyes. From a child she had danced the magic of the ballets, where love was an enchantment, with a dreamlike quality about it. She could not believe that real life love was like that.

She shrank physically from the very thought of being captive in the arms of a demanding man, at the mercy of his wilful strength.

'I think I should hate to be married more than anything else on this earth.' She said it fiercely. 'I'm not like Dove. I don't want my wings clipped by any man.'

'What if you should fall in love?' he murmured.

'Love only happens if you want it to. Love doesn't approach unless you beckon to it.'

'Are you quite certain of that, *matushka*?'

'I am certain of what I want, and what I don't want.'

'Then why are you so afraid to commit yourself to a dinner *à deux* with me, if we should be obliged to spend the next few hours together?'

'I'm disinterested, Prince Anton.'

'No, Miss Devrel, you are afraid to put your own theory to the test. If you remain aloof from men, then you are unlikely to fall in love. But if you permit yourself the company of a man——'

'You think you are so irresistible?' she gasped.

'No man is that, Miss Devrel, but when we walk from this lift certain whispers are going to follow at your heels. People will wonder why you were here at the hotel in the first place. They will suppose that you came to call on me.'

'My sister can easily repudiate that little speculation!'

'Will you wish the smoke of a little fire to drift in her direction?'

Chrys stared at him ... and there stole into her mind a picture of Jeremy Stanton's mother, that awful, snobbish woman whom Dove was daring to take on for love of the son.

'You are a devil, Prince Anton,' she said. 'You know how to hit a sensitive nerve.'

'Yes.' The word was quietly enough spoken, but suddenly he stirred, moved, and sent rippling through the air a breath of danger as from a leopard caged.

A cage that stayed firmly suspended in mid-air, while down there on the ground people looked at each other, and knew by now from the porter on the penthouse floor that a girl was alone in the lift with Anton de Casenove ... the man whom an angry Frenchman had shot through the heart ... the man with a reputation as dangerous as his face.

'Come, agree to dine with me *demain soir*. Forget for once that you hate men.'

She looked at him expecting mockery, and saw instead a pair of grey eyes veiled in the smoke of the cheroot he had just lit up.

'You are very sure of yourself, *milor*,' she said.

'Do you think so, Miss Devrel?' His smile was enigmatical. 'Only destiny really knows what tomorrow may bring.'

'It's tonight I'm worried about!'

'Is it?' he drawled. 'Don't you take me for a gentleman?'

'Would you advise me to bet on that, *milor*?'

His answer was a smile, half veiled by smoke; half veiled by the dark lashes shading his smoky grey eyes ... a smile which confirmed for Chrys what she had felt from the moment she had noticed him across the sky lounge.

Under that suave veneer, that smooth dark suiting, there lurked an untamed heart in a graceful, untamed body.

CHAPTER THREE

'DARLING, enjoy his company but don't fall in love with him!'

Those words of Dove's echoed through Chrys's mind as the cab she had just picked up sped through the gaily lighted West End to the Adonis Club on the south bank, across whose dancing terrace the breezes of the River Thames wafted.

Needless to say Chrys had scoffed at the idea of losing her contained young heart to a *roué*, no matter how darkly attractive he was; no matter how gallant he could *act* when walking out of a lift with her at one o'clock in the morning and kissing her hand for the benefit of those who had stayed to watch the rescue.

The incident had got into the daily papers, and there had been a coy reference to the wedding bells on the bag Chrys had held clutched in her hand. She smiled a little to herself as she thought of Prince Anton and his possible reaction to the speculation of the newsmen. She didn't imagine for one moment that he was a born bachelor, but when he married he would choose someone a little more passionate than herself, she was sure of that.

She sat self-contained in the cab as it halted in a traffic jam near the Mermaid Theatre, where Tarquin Powers was starring in *Macbeth*. She leaned to the window and gazed at the large poster with his distinguished face and figure on it. Like herself that great actor was dedicated to his art ... a career in the arts did not mix with marriage ... not a marriage that involved the total involvement of the heart.

She leaned back in her seat as the cab proceeded on its way to the Club, and a street light that slanted into the enclosure revealed the cool silvery material of her dress, and the wrap of pale velvet against which her coiled hair gleamed softly. In her earlobes there were little flame-coloured gems, and deep blue were her eyes, with flying wings of eyeshadow painted above them.

It was while she was dressing that Dove had come into her bedroom and made her profound little remark. 'Fall in love with *him*?' Chrys had laughed. 'He's the type who breaks female hearts as he breaks in Arab fillies. He's been brought up to think of women as chattels ... objects of pleasure.'

'Then why are you dining with him?' Dove had asked, reasonably.

'Because we made a bet, the prince and I. He said the lift wouldn't move before midnight, and I said it would. He won, and so I must pay the forfeit.'

'Dinner at the Adonis, eh? They say it's all rigged out just like those clubs of the Georgian era, where Beau Brummel and the other rakes used to dine in alcoves with their "ladies of the night".'

'Thanks!' Once again Chrys had laughed, but in her heart she had wondered what real motive lay behind the prince's invitation. 'I should think he already knows I'm not a "lady of the night" after being locked in a lift with me for eight hours.'

'Chrys, whatever did you do?' For about the fiftieth time Dove had looked at her as if it were impossible to

41

be imprisoned with such a man and emerge with her virtue intact.

'We talked,' Chrys repeated. 'Do I have to convince you, Dove? He's as good at talking as I imagine he is at most things, including casting doubt over a girl's good name! Do assure Jeremy's mother that her beloved son is not marrying into the family of a scarlet woman. In fact, to put it quite bluntly I couldn't imagine a man as suave as the prince enjoying love's antics on the hard floor of an express lift.'

'Chrys, really!' Dove had looked quite shocked.

'Well, it was what you were wondering, now wasn't it, my pet?' It was then, with a touch of bravado, that Chrys had added the flame-coloured earbobs to her ensemble. She had bought them in Russia off a gipsy fortune-teller, who had looked deep in her eyes and warned her about a tall, dark man. She had laughed at the time, because it was so to formula—beware of the dark stranger—he will bring you love or danger!

It was as Chrys had viewed the earbobs in the mirror, and set them sparkling against her hair with a little defiant toss of her head, that Dove had announced her intention of sending a wedding invitation to the prince.

'It will conciliate Mrs Stanton,' she said. 'She's a bit of a snob and his title will overwhelm her.'

'Which one?' Chrys said drily. 'He's also known as Zain ben Sharife, and Jeremy's mama might imagine that he'll sweep her off to his desert abode in the manner of that silent-screen actor—what was his name, Rudolph Valentino? Mrs Stanton probably remembers him.'

They had joked about it, Dove and herself, but tiny

flickers of curiosity and doubt were like sparks in Chrys's veins when she alighted from the cab at the discreetly lit entrance of the Adonis Club. She paid her fare, then turned to find a bewigged and knee-breeched doorman holding open the bowed-glass entrance door so that she might step into the Regency-decorated foyer of the restaurant.

She had specified that she meet the prince on the premises of the club, wishing for as long as possible to conceal from him the address of the Kensington flat she shared with Dove. There was no knowing what Dove might say to him if they were to meet! She was the type of girl, pampered for her prettiness, who said naïvely whatever came into her mind. She might ask Anton de Casenove if his intentions were as honourable as Jeremy's, and Chrys was appalled by the very thought of what he might assume.

He might take it into his mocking head to think she had designs on his bachelorhood!

'Your mask, *madame*.'

'I beg your—a mask?' She stared at the white velvet half-mask the bewigged attendant in the foyer had placed in her hands.

'It is a rule of the Adonis Club, *madame*. Each patron must be masked.'

'How romantic!' She had been about to say 'how ridiculous', but thought better of it when she saw a tall, lean, elegant figure reflected in one of the long Regency mirrors of the foyer. His evening suit was perfection, his ruffled shirt-front impeccable, his narrow feet shod by a master hand. And though he wore a black strip of velvet across his upper face, she knew his figure, and the faintly mocking smile on his mouth.

The attendant took her wrap, and the prince advanced towards her with all the silent suppleness of a duellist ... for all the time he duelled with his eyes and his words, and perhaps his intentions.

As he came closer to her, her nerves quivered like water when a sudden breeze passes over it. Now those subtle grey eyes were appraising her through the openings of his mask, studying her dress with its shapely hanging sleeves and its design that was so simple as to be medieval. The material had been purchased in Russia, and the design had been seen in a stained window of the old Russian castle where she and the other members of the Company had danced a ballet one memorable evening.

She knew from the look in the masked grey eyes that the prince admired her dress, but all he said as he bowed his head with that flawless perfection of manner was that he welcomed her and was glad to see that she had not lost her nerve and left him to eat and drink alone.

'You must put on your mask before we go into the restaurant. Shall I assist you, Miss Devrel?'

'Are the masks in the tradition of the Regency rakes, *milor*?'

'Quite so. To be seen but not recognised was all part of the game.'

'What game is that?' she asked, retreating ever so slightly as she adjusted the white velvet mask and saw his face, in the golden light of the Regency chandeliers, take on a demonic quality, partly mocking, and yet with something intent about the set of the lips and the glint in the eyes.

'The game of illusion, *matushka*. Of sadness masked

in gaiety. Of devilry masked in piety. Of hate masked in love.'

'I see.' She stood there slim and silvery, with only the scarlet earbobs to light her pale beauty. 'And what mask are you wearing, Prince Anton?'

'Only the one you see.' A smile flickered on his lips as he touched the strip of black velvet across his upper face.

As she thought over his remark a teasing silence hung between them for a few moments, then a waiter appeared at his elbow and murmured a few deferential words.

'Our table is ready in the Alcove du Diable, so shall we go in, Miss Devrel?'

'Yes,' she said, and felt her heartbeats under the fine taut silk of her dress as she followed the waiter to their table and felt the prince walking so tall and silently at her side. Dark velvet curtains across the doorway of the alcove were thrust aside so they could enter, and inside a table was beautifully set in front of a banquette, and a soft illumination came from the shaded wall-lights.

The alcove was private, intimate, and as she felt the admiring flick of the waiter's eyes over her person, the little jolt to her nerves told her that he thought she was the prince's *inamorata*. It was the inevitable supposition in view of his rakish reputation, and as she sat down on the banquette and smoothed her dress, she noticed there were orchids on the table. A cluster of them meshed in fern, creamy pale with a merest dusting of gold at the edges of their secretive petals.

Instinct told her that the prince had ordered them; that they weren't a speciality of the club like the face masks and the Regency satyrs and cupids decorating the ceiling of the Alcove du Diable.

'*Champagneskaye,*' said the prince, as he sat down beside her, using the Russian word with a sort of love in his voice. 'And baby oysters on the shell.'

He turned briefly to Chrys. 'You will allow me to select your *hors d'oeuvre?*'

'Yes, if you wish to do so.' She was slightly confused to find him close to her on the seat, looking so directly at her through the oblique openings in his black velvet mask. He had the kind of face that suited a mask, for it brought out the fine shaping of his lips, and the firm sculpturing of his jaw. It emphasised the mystery, and the charismatic quality of the man. Made her even more aware of his unique accent, and fascinating turn of phrase. She turned to the orchids, with their quieter exoticism, and touched her fingers to the strange pale petals rimmed with gold.

'Champagne and oysters, *monsieur.*' The waiter withdrew and the portières fell into place behind his dark-clad figure. At once the sense of intimacy was provocative, made more so than last night in the lift because Chrys was wearing silk and eye-shadow and a whisper of her best perfume. And they were seated together on the soft leather of a banquette and orchids out of season were on the dining table.

'You look very lovely, Chrysdova,' he said. 'Like a figure which has stepped out of a medieval window in a quiet, mysterious chapel. Even your hair has the authentic styling, and the only note out of tune—ah, but perhaps I am being too personal. The blunt British are reserved about themselves, eh?'

She turned her head to look at him, provoked by his remark about her appearance. What could be out of

46

tune when she had spent a couple of hours getting ready for this dinner with him? 'What little thing displeases you, *milor*?' she asked pertly.

'These, of course.' He flicked a finger at the scarlet earbobs. 'You should wear only sapphires, the very darkest, with a blue flame burning in the heart of them.'

'I could hardly afford sapphires on the money I earn.' She jerked away from his touch, and consequently the tiny red gems danced gaily against the gold of her hair. 'If it offends your taste to be seen with a woman in jewellery which has not come from Cartier, then I can leave this instant without a qualm or a backward glance.'

'You will stay exactly where you are, you little spitfire.' His lip quirked, but there was a looming danger to his wide, impeccably tailored shoulders which warned her to remain seated. The wall lighting slanted on to his face and he seemed tawny-skinned, and the sculpturing of his cheekbones was intensified. He had the looks of a man who could be cruel when it came to having his own way with a woman.

'No woman walks out on me,' he drawled. 'Later on I might grow bored and send you home in a cab, but right now I am intrigued by the look of you, and by the antagonism I arouse in you.'

'I suppose it must come as a shock to you not to be turning my head with your practised charm and your sophistication, Prince Anton? Or do you have a desert name by which you prefer to be called? Somehow you strike me as a man who regards women as *harem* slaves, to be enjoyed one hour and ignored the next.'

'I had no idea, Miss Devrel, that you were such an

authority on the men of the East, or of the West.' His drawl was infinitely mocking. 'When you told me last night that you hated men, I took it to mean that you had ice crystals in your veins, but now I begin to wonder if your coolness is the result of passion spent on the wrong man.'

'Men have never bothered me,' she retorted. 'All I have ever wanted is to dance every dramatic role in ballet, but I am sure you wouldn't understand about dedication to anything. To you, *milor*, life is a game and pleasure is your pastime. You are like Adonis, ever chasing, and ever fleeing the trap of Venus. Like Adonis you bled for love, but being also something of a devil you lived to chase and run again.'

'From you?' he mocked. 'After I have chased you, of course.'

A scornful answer sprang to her lips, but was checked as the portières opened and the waiter appeared with their champagne and oysters. The next few minutes were devoted to the opening of the wine, the tasting and the pouring of it into the wine bowls on the long stems, ideal for collecting the bubbles at the edge of the wide rims. The small oysters, pale pink in colour, were served on the shells of giant oysters, with a mayonnaise sauce and slivers of lemon, slices of crusty bread and balls of butter.

Despite the antagonism which he aroused so readily in Chrys, she watched fascinated as the prince tasted the wine and pronounced it perfect in his flawless French; then he examined each shell of oysters to make certain they were of the very best, and finally he dismissed the waiter with an imperious yet in no way demeaning flick of his hand. He was a man accustomed to giving orders, and having them obeyed with the minimum of fuss and the requisite of perfection.

Chrys felt the stab of realisation that he wasn't just anyone, and colour tingled in her cheeks as she accepted the pepper mill from him and recalled the way she had just spoken to him. Adonis—and Venus! The colour deepened in her cheeks. She had more or less implied that his looks condemned him to be a lover, whereas at heart he was really scornful of love. This placed her in the position of Venus, the one who was hungry for love!

She looked at him with a flash to her eyes, all on edge in case he should think for one moment that she saw him in the light of a lover. He returned her look with almost too much innocence, and then he raised his wine glass.

'Come, Chrysdova, drink a toast with me!'

Obediently she picked up her glass and felt it quiver in her nervous fingers.

'To the sham pains of life, *matushka*, and may you rarely know the real ones.'

'It would be nice not to know them, *milor*, but——' She shuddered as she remembered the agony of her fall, the rack of pain on which she had lain in the speeding ambulance, the terror of finding her legs so useless ... until the blessed relief of that first movement all those days after the operation.

'Drink your champagne,' he said quietly. 'It has a way of blurring the reality of things.'

She was tempted to retort that she had tasted champagne before accepting the honour of dining with him, but the moment she put her lips to her wine glass she knew that she had never tasted champagne like this before. It was like liquid gold, with a sensuous quality ... it was like everything else he demanded of life, a perfect wine.

'I see that you are a connoisseur, *milor*.' By now she had fallen into the habit of addressing him in this Regency way, for try as she might she couldn't accept Anton de Casenove as a modern man. He had the locks and the rakish dignity of those Georgian gentlemen of leisure and refined pleasure. The cut and style of his suits had a quiet flamboyance about them, and as he ate his oysters off the small silver fork, she noticed his dark-stoned cufflinks, and the seal ring on the small finger of his left hand, engraved with a strange Islamic symbol.

There was not a single item about the man that was ordinary ... least of all his conversation.

'You are wondering, *petite*, all the time about my motive in wishing you to take dinner with me, and I wonder why you should find it a mystery when a thousand men could give you the reason in three simple words.'

'But you don't deal in simplicities, Prince Anton. You are too subtle for that, and last night you didn't ask me in plain terms to dine with you. You made of it a thing of chance.'

'But I had to do so.' His eyebrow quirked above the darkness of his mask. 'You would not be here in the Alcove du Diable if I had not coerced you. Now would you?'

'Perhaps not.' She shrugged her shoulders and the silk of her dress glimmered in the soft lighting that illuminated their table; there was a gravity to her blue eyes as they dwelt on his face. 'I am not a girl who goes out on many dates. My ballet régime has always been a strict one, imposed by my first important ballet-master and kept up by me. The dedicated dancer never dances out of theatre hours.'

'How wistful your eyes look when you speak of dancing.' The prince drank from his wine glass and studied her eyes as he spoke, the blueness of them intensified by the white mask. 'Has your surgeon vetoed all dancing, or only your professional activity?'

'Oh, I'm quite fit for normal activity, but as you probably know from your grandmother, the art of ballet is pretty strenuous and I mustn't do the bending and limb stretching involved ... not for a year!'

'A year in the desert is but a day in the city.' Again he spoke in a voice almost as smooth as velvet. 'So the gaieties of other female hearts are of less importance to you, eh?'

'I'm not a gay person, *mon cher*.' She smiled a little as she spoke and ate her last oyster. 'They were delicious ... do you always demand the very best from life, Prince Anton?'

'It is in my nature to do so.' His lips smiled beneath the mask, but it seemed to her that his eyes had the stillness of the sea when a storm has passed and left a certain melancholy in the air. 'You are correct in your estimation of your own personality. Gay people are of the surface, like a frothy soda drink. You are deep ... still waters ... with possibilities unseen and undisturbed. No man, of course, has ever touched you, and I don't mean in a physical sense. There have been men, no doubt, who have kissed you?'

'Are you being curious, *milor*, or are you being personal?'

51

'Both.' He reached to the wall and pressed a small button for the return of the waiter. She knew that other couples were dining close by, and yet the portières seemed to muffle all sound and it was intensely intimate to be here like this, being asked such questions by a man so worldly, and yet at the same time so primitive.

Chrys was startled by the thought ... he wore his perfectly tailored evening suit as if it were a second skin, and yet she sensed a restlessness in him, a barely suppressed desire to wrench open the tie and black silk at his throat, to toss back his head and breathe a free wild air in a wild and open place.

'When do you return to the desert?' she surprised herself by asking.

'Soon—perhaps in a month from now.'

'I have the feeling you can't wait to see and smell the sands again. You are like a sailor who while at sea longs for dry land, but as soon as he comes ashore he finds himself hemmed in, restricted by the civilities of civilised living. You appear to be incredibly sophisticated, *milor*, but I believe you are really a Tartar.'

He inclined his head and laughed so softly in his throat that it was almost a purring sound. 'The *steppes* are in my blood and the freedom of the desert supplies my need for what I cannot have in reality. I visit Russia, but I cannot live there ... it is not my person but my spirit which is exiled from the land of my grandparents. You understand?'

She nodded, and was glad when the waiter reappeared to dispel the air of seriousness which had crept into the alcove. The waiter carried two large menu cards, but with a slightly lazy smile she requested the prince to choose for her. 'You are the epicure, *milor.*'

'*En effet*,' he rather mockingly agreed, and for an intent moment his eyes looked directly into hers, and from that look there sped through her person the quick-silver awareness that he thought her a rather beautiful object ... something which he might desire to possess ... perhaps for an hour. Immediately her eyes went as cool as ice, and the soft shimmer of her dress was like a coating of ice over her slender figure. She sat very straight against the dark leather of the banquette, entirely untouchable, virgin as fresh fallen snow ... only the gems in her earlobes had animation in that moment.

Then he looked at the menu card and began to order their meal in his impeccable French. Fresh asparagus and Irish salmon, with tiny new potatoes ... the delicious, almost simple food of the epicure, following the richness of the oysters and champagne. Finally richness again when he chose fruits *au kirsch*, and coffee with Armagnac.

'You have wined and dined me,' said Chrys with a smile that was still a little cool, 'like one of those dancers of the Edwardian era, who were so underpaid that they lived almost on birdseed all day and relied on the stage-door admirers to keep them from starving to death.'

'Really?' he drawled. 'Is that how you regard me, as a stage-door admirer? And what did the little dancers do after the supper *à deux*? Did they pay with kisses and pleasure?'

'Very likely,' she said. 'But if you are expecting a similar kind of repayment then you are in for a disappointment, *milor*. I dined with you because I lost a bet not because I needed the food, delicious as it was.'

'I am pleased you found the food to your liking, at least.' There was a quirk to his lips as he raised the cognac glass, but a faint angry flare to his nostrils as he breathed the aroma of the Armagnac. 'You are a cool one, Miss Devrel. You need the lash of love to break the ice around your heart.'

'All I need,' she retorted, 'is to find a job in which I can bury my feelings for a year, until I can get back to the thing I love. There are different sorts of love, and you as a man of the world must know it.'

'Perhaps.' And then very curtly he broke the epicure's rule and tossed back his cognac in a single gulp, as if it were vodka. 'You find physical fulfilment in dancing ... you find love in the applause which your dancing receives. That is because you have not yet met love in the guise of a man ... ah, you think it couldn't happen?'

'I am making no bets with you, Prince Anton.' She gave a slight laugh. 'All my life I have wanted only to be a dancer, unique like Fonteyn, poetic and perfect in line and action. I dare not love——'

'Ah, what a significant word, *matushka*. Does your heart warn you that you might love a man with a greater force than you love the dance?'

'No,' she denied, 'not at all. Men are all alike. They want a slave, a meek and willing keeper of the home and the hearth. Their egos demand that the domestic slave produce a child, and then another, ensuring that the slave is doubly enslaved. Oh, I know for girls like Dove, my sister, this is a kind of heaven on earth, but I —I'd stifle if my body and my soul were tied to the

54

stove and the cot, and the demands of a man!'

'You shuddered when you said that, *matushka*.' He leaned a little towards her, and there was a danger to him, and a subtle knowing quality that made her cry of the heart seem the cry of a child who had yet to grow up. 'Are you afraid of lovemaking? Afraid it will dispossess you of your "slim gilt soul" in your slim, white body?'

'Stop it!' Her words were a whisper and a cry. 'You have no right to speak to me in such a way!'

'And why not? There are women who find their excitement in such conversation.'

'I don't.' Her eyes blazed through the openings of her mask. 'All I want right now is to go home!'

'Don't be a child,' he rejoined. 'The night is young and I intend first to dance with you, and then to take you for a long cool drive. For once in your self-contained, planned and passionless life you will let someone else rule you, if only for a few hours. Now relax from all that tension which is making your pupils dilate and your heart beat too quickly for comfort. Relax!'

She stared at him a moment longer, then gradually she leaned back against the soft leather of the banquette. 'I—I had an idea you could dance. It's in the way you walk.'

'I am very fond of the pastime.' He leaned back himself, his *demi-tasse* of coffee in his lean, well-shaped hand. 'With a grandmother such as mine there was always music in the house and she had me taught all manner of dancing when I was a child. Miroslava was never a woman to displease, for her smile was as lovely as her anger was terrible. A true Cossack woman, composed of honey and iron. Anyway, I liked to dance, especially as I grew older and could tango and foxtrot with attractive girls.'

His lips smiled nostalgically beneath the black rim of his mask. 'I did not go to public school. I had a tutor until I went off to college who had been a Guards officer; a rake with women, but with a brilliant mind. He and Miroslava between them made a man of me before I was sixteen.' His mouth as he spoke those words became a dangerous one, with a glint of hard white teeth. '*Leben seele* was the motto of my German tutor. Life is soul, and soul is life—so live it! I have lived, *matushka*, and you can also say that I have died.'

She gazed at him as if mesmerised, and his face in that moment had a cruel dark beauty. He was everything her training, her upbringing and her instinct fought against. She wanted to leave with all her mind, yet her body was excited by the thought of dancing with him. Oh, how long it had been! Weeks since she had known the heaven of music in her limbs and the delight that only dancing could give her. She would have wanted to die if they had told her at the clinic that she could never dance again ... and now had come the moment when she could dance again, if not as a ballerina, at least as a woman.

A woman ... in the arms of Anton de Casenove!

CHAPTER FOUR

'WELL, have I set your mind somewhat at rest, and made your feet impatient to dance?' he asked abruptly. 'I hope your *cri du coeur* is no longer that I take you home?'

'You learned well from your tutor, didn't you?' She gave a rueful little laugh. 'Even as you give a woman what she wants, you lay on the lash.'

He shrugged and finished his coffee. 'I grew up among Arabs, who regard women as mettlesome as horses. It does only harm to feed a woman and a horse with too much sugar.'

'The comparison is hardly flattering. I hope you don't think, *milor*, that I shall trample all over you in my friskiness on the dance floor?'

'That is hardly likely, *matushka*. I saw you dance at the Bolshoi—and it occurs to me how my *baboushka* would have enjoyed that. She would indeed find a cool angelic creature like you, Miss Devrel, enjoyable to shock.'

'You are speaking of your grandmother?'

'Yes. She would say to you "the key to life is love of it" and tell you there is no harm in tasting the wine of every experience, so long as you avoid the dregs.' He moved his mobile hands in an expressive gesture. 'It is being alive that counts, whether it brings pain or gives rapture. Desire itself is a crucifix—ah, but you have your heart fixed on dreams not on reality.'

'At least I harm no one with my philosophy,' she said.

'But is it any fun for a girl to be so miraculously virtuous? What has held the men at bay? Ah, but you don't need to tell me—it is that cool hauteur, that tilt to the chin, that threat of the sand cat in your eyes that exactly match the darkest sapphire. Do you wish to dance with me?'

'I dislike modern dancing,' she said, even as anticipation leapt alight in her veins and there was a tingling in her toes racing upwards through her slim dancing legs.

'So do I, *matushka*. Do you want more coffee, or are you replete?'

'Quite replete, *milor*. It was a splendid dinner, thank you very much.'

'*Bon*.' He rang the bell for the waiter, and while he was engaged in settling the bill and commenting favourably on the food and wine, Chrys took a swift look at her face in the tiny mirror of her powder-case. She ran the tongue of her lipstick around her lips, and tried to be as composed as her companion would allow. She knew he was looking at her, watching each of her movements with those smoky eyes that held elements of the dramatic, the mysterious, and the subtle.

They were eyes that would look terrible in real and overwhelming anger ... eyes that would smoulder with all the passions of his fierce inheritance when he held a woman in his arms.

Soon ... quite soon he would hold her in his arms when they danced. As the waiter held aside the portières and they left the alcove she could hear the dance music drifting from the terrace which overlooked the oldest, most historic river in England. The river upon which the carved barques of royalty had sailed to and from the palaces; to gilded and gay receptions ... and to the block, and the dark-masked axeman at the royal Tower.

A tremor ran all through Chrys as they stepped on to the terrace and she saw the masked couples dancing so close in each other's arms. The atmosphere was seductive, with the river running by and glimmering in the dim light of the lamps along the balustrade of the terrace. The orchestra was concealed so that the music seemed to be in the air itself rather than played by musicians.

Chrys tautened as an arm encircled her waist and she was drawn so inevitably against the smooth dark suiting of the prince, against the lean suppleness of his body, her limbs and her body responding to him at once, as if he were her partner in a *pas de deux* instead of her partner in a foxtrot.

Anton de Casenove was a devil without a doubt, but in his blood and his bones ran the inheritance of rhythm from Miroslava herself, and he danced like an angel. The wonder of it was like a magic igniting Chrys so that within seconds, no more, they were dancing as if they were one person. He had all the mastery, all the control of some of her best ballet partners, with that wonderful strength in the legs, that instinct that guided a girl through the most intricate steps. And the foxtrot could be wonderfully intricate, and inexpressibly evocative as the music played ... a music from another time, when war had swept Europe and sons and lovers had choked in the mud of battlefields, where

soon masses of poppies had grown as if to defy death
with their scarlet beauty.

'Poor butterfly,
      In the blossoms waiting. . . .'

Chrys was lost in the music as it went from one past
melody to another; it was an incredible delight to be so
in step with his man who so antagonised her at other
times. His guidance was so sure and strong so that her
body knew instinctively that it could enjoy the fabulous pleasure of dancing without a moment of fear that
suddenly the disintegrating pain would flare in her
spine and her legs would give way beneath her.

She was in a kind of heaven and when at last the
music ceased she came down to earth almost too
abruptly.

'No——' The word broke from her in protest. 'I
want to go on and on——'

'No!' He spoke firmly and led her from the terrace.
'You have danced for an hour and that is sufficient.'

'It was so perfect—oh, please, Anton!' She spoke his
name almost unaware. 'Please, let us stay! Let us go
on dancing!'

'You mustn't overtire yourself.' Now they were in
the foyer and he removed the mask from her brilliantly
blue eyes and looked down into them ... unseen by
her because she was still in that rapt, enchanted mood
in which dancing always left her. It was as if she stood
in the wings of a theatre as the applause died away and
the curtain fell for the last time ... strung to go on, to
dance and dance until her body ached and her toes
were on fire.

'Come, we will go for a drive!' Her velvet wrap was
clasped about her shoulders, and something soft and

scented brushed her cheek. With a little shiver of realisation she saw the prince being helped into a topcoat,
and felt under her hand the curled petals of the
orchids which had decorated their table. Now they
were pinned to her wrap, and the prince was unmasked
and looking at her with intent and glinting eyes.

'They are bringing round the car,' he said, and very
casually he took a blade-thin cheroot case from his
pocket and opened it. He selected one of the dark Russian cheroots, and immediately the foyer attendant was
at his elbow flourishing a lighter. Smoke jetted from
the imperious nostrils and the faint, strange perfume
of the orchids was drowned in the aroma of the
cheroot.

'Is it late?' she asked.

'Not too late,' he said enigmatically.

The attendant held open the door and they went out
into the night air, cool against her skin, golden from
the tall lamps along the embankment. In the kerb there
stood a long, racy car in a bronze colour. Chrys hesi-
tated and stood by the tonneau of the sleek car, a pale,
silvery figure with questions in her eyes. 'Where are we
going?' she asked him.

'Somewhere—anywhere. What does it matter? You
are not Cinderella who has to be gone by midnight, are
you?' A quizzical smile gleamed deep in his eyes as he
regarded her in the amber light. 'All that finery will
not turn to rags, I trust?'

'My sister will be wondering about me.'

'Why, because you are with a man of uncertain reputation?'

'Something like that. Dove is the anxious sort.'

'A dove by name and nature, eh?' He glanced at his

61

thin gold wristwatch. 'It should not unduly ruffle her gentle feathers if I take you for a spin in my new car? It was delivered this morning and I am having it shipped to the Middle East in a few days, so I wish to enjoy it like a new toy. Don't you like it?'

She turned to look at the rakish lines of it, and saw that the top was back and that the upholstery was leopard-pelted. A smile touched her lips. There was a streak of the exhibitionist in *milor*.

'It's very sleek, and has an air of danger about it,' she replied. 'It suits your personality.'

'Is it my dangerous personality, *matushka*, which makes you hesitate to take a drive with me?' His voice had softened to that husky purr and he had drawn a little nearer to her, silently, until suddenly her wrists were locked in his fingers. 'You danced with me. You enjoyed that with every nerve in your body. Do you think I don't know? That I didn't feel your pleasure?'

'I—I hadn't danced for so long.' Her eyes met his, resistant and deeply blue; her breath quickened. 'Yes, it made me happy to dance.'

'Will it make you less happy to drive in an open car with me?' he quizzed her. 'My hands, this time, will be occupied with the wheel, and my thoughts with the road and the other traffic.'

'You make me sound a prude.' She gave a slight laugh and pulled free of him and went to the car. She opened the door and slipped inside ... he was too tantalising to argue with, and she didn't really wish to end yet this fascinatingly dangerous evening. Being with Anton de Casenove was like being on the edge of a volcano, or within range of the unpredictable temper of a leopard. She gave a little sigh and settled down in her seat ... but he danced divinely, the devil, and she could dislike no man who moved as if his muscles were of silk and steel. Her artistic nature was at the mercy of his lean and fascinating grace ... she wouldn't think of the *roué* in him which had climbed forbidden balconies.

They drove away from the Adonis Club, and the night wind blew the soft hair from her brow. A half-hour spin with him wouldn't hurt, she told herself. He wasn't to know that Dove was spending the night at her fiancé's home, where discussions regarding the forthcoming wedding were to be held with the forthright Mrs Stanton presiding and directing in a way which Chrys would have rebelled against, had she been the bride-to-be.

She smiled a little to herself ... how easy on the system to be malleable like Dove, but she would sooner have her own flashfire temperament and independence. It wouldn't suit her to be a dove by nature.

'It is a fine night,' said the man at her side, who drove the Rapier as he did everything else, with the skill, verve and style of the man who feared no one, not even Destiny herself. 'On a night such as this in the desert I would be riding instead of driving. Can you ride, Miss Devrel?'

'Yes.' It was faintly disconcerting the way he switched from the informality of calling her 'little one' in Russian back to the formality of her surname. 'Dove and I had riding ponies when we were quite young. My father has always worked for the local council and my mother liked us to have "nice things" and to be a little more privileged than she was herself when a girl. You understand?'

'Indubitably.' There wasn't the faintest hint of mockery in his voice and he sounded quite kind. 'You have a nice mother ... my own was selfishly gay and in the divorce court long before I had my first long trousers.'

'I'm so sorry.' She cast him a sympathetic side-glance, but his profile was as hard and fine as that upon a bronze coin. She knew at once that he had long since ceased to regret the legal loss of his mother, but she felt certain that he had never tried to fight the gay and wilful instincts inherited from her.

'Are you wondering about my father?' he asked, and the car sped smoothly along as he spoke, and the street lights were less clustering, as if they were heading out of London. 'He was a finer man than I am, who devoted much of his life to the Sheik's people, and who died one hot *khamsin* day when the North African campaign was in full swing. He was decorated for bravery, and his memory is cherished by the people of El Kezar. They expect me to live up to him, of course, but quite frankly I am not a saint. I sometimes think that if he had given to my mother the devotion and the passion which he gave to the Oasis, she might never have looked at another man. He married her, placed her upon a pedestal, and then was surprised when she toppled into the arms of a French artist who came to North Africa to paint the Ouled Naïl dancers, and the Arabian cavalry, and all the wonders I remember from my boyhood. Much has changed, of course. The province is now state governed, and the fruits of the Oasis are so heavily taxed that profits are a laugh. But I still have the house in which Miroslava lived as a Sheik's friend. The house called Belle Tigresse!'

'What a provocative name, *milor.*' Chrys looked at him, and then at the wide highway along which they were travelling so swiftly, so smoothly that the engine made hardly a sound. It was as if the engine of the car was wrapped in velvet ... the same velvet that seemed to enwrap the surrounding fields. Her heartbeats quickened. She wanted to ask him to head back to London, but she was strangely afraid of him and his unpredictable nature. If she showed fear of him now, he might dash the car into the nearest lay-by and give her every reason for being afraid. She strove to sit calmly beside him ... she sensed that he was waiting for her to panic ... this *beau tigre* of a man!

'It is a provocative house, *matushka*. All of white stone, you understand, with one entire wall and tower enshrouded in scarlet bougainvillaea which Miroslava had planted ... perhaps to remind her of her passionate Prince Ivanyi, who died in his white uniform, cut down by sabres on the steps of the Czarist palace the first day of the uprising. *Magnifique! Comme il faut.*'

'I think it terrible,' she retorted, 'that a man and a woman should be parted in such a tragic way!'

'Ah, there speaks the romantic! And now, *matushka*, I have discovered in my devious way why you remain the ice maiden who has never melted for a man. You are looking, yourself, for a *preux chevalier.*'

'I am doing nothing of the sort, *milor.* A man would interfere in every way with my career in ballet. He would expect me to make *him* my career!'

'But you might fall in love with a dancing partner,' drawled the prince, and still the car sped smoothly through the night, on towards the coast, it seemed, with London now left far behind them. Chrys cast a rather wild look behind her, and her hair flew in a gold wing, breaking loose from its chignon as the wind soared towards her. She gave a gasp, half fear, and half delight to be travelling along like this, in a swift car commanded by a man who drove fast but who broke not a rule in the driver's handbook. It was as if he had an instinct for going through life on the knife-edge of danger . . . only once had he come to grief, and that had been through a woman.

Chrys thrust the loosened hair from her eyes and wondered briefly if love had blunted, for once, his instinct for enjoying danger without having it touch him?

'Male ballet dancers are as dedicated as the females,' she said. 'To dance in ballet is to be at the mercy of the dance. Of course, there are one or two exceptional marriages within the world of ballet, but they are love matches in the grand tradition and would survive despite the demands imposed by the régime of the dance. Famous male dancers such as Lonza and Dantoni are also famous for their love affairs, and though it's marvellous when one is lucky enough to have the Panther for a partner, a sensible girl avoids becoming involved emotionally.'

'Sensible!' muttered the prince. 'What a very British word it is! Like hotpot and pudding with gravy! Well, tonight I am teaching you that too much sensibility will blunt your natural sense of gaiety. Ah yes, it is there, the gaiety, like small blue devils in the eyes. You desire with one half of you to enjoy this drive without inhibition, but the primly obedient and dedicated half of you is terrified that the wind is combing out your hair into the wild silk which you have been taught to keep meticulously neat and orderly. What is this dance régime? Some sort of novitiate, for which you take vows of devotion and sublimation?'

'Of course not!' she had to laugh, albeit with a touch of nerves and temper. 'There are rules attached to everything, but you are a natural rebel, *milor*, so you wouldn't understand. To love something is to be enslaved.'

'But you would rebel against enslavement to a man,' he argued. 'You prefer the inhumanity of pirouettes upon the tips of your toes, and the arabesques that would seem like torment to your audience. You know, I have heard Miroslava say that for hours after dancing she has lain in a torpor of sheer exhaustion, with every muscle aching and in revolt against the merciless demands of the dance. Do you really think that a man would put you through such torment in his arms?'

Chrys tautened where she sat, and stared at the dark shapely profile of the prince, outlined now and again by the infrequent tall lamps at the roadside.

'W-what are you implying?' she asked, and she felt the shock in her body, and heard it in her words. What did he mean? And where was he taking her?

'Oh come, Chrysdova, you are not that unworldly.'

'Look, if you are planning some sort of a—a seduction——'

'As if I would?' He laughed in that purring and infuriating way, as if laughter were an inward thing and never a bellow; a secret to be shared with himself but never with her.

'You would, if you felt like it!' Anger and nerves shook her voice. 'Where are we going? To some hideaway you have in the country, where you take your ladies of the night? I'm warning you—if you dare to touch me I'll tear out those devil eyes of yours!'

'I'm sure of it, little sand cat.' But still he softly laughed as if illimitably sure of his own strength and his practised ability to overcome the resistance of a mere woman. 'We are on the road to Kent, which is very attractive at this time of the year, with the fruit on the trees and the sunrise so colourful over the Bay of Sandwich.'

'Kent!'

'Yes, do you know it?'

'I know that never in my life have I met anyone with your gall! Turn the car this instant and take me back to Kensington!'

'It sounds like a song,' he rejoined, 'from the music halls, *hein?* "*Take me back to Kensington as quickly as you can. Oh, Prince Anton, you are a naughty man!*"'

'The word "naughty" when applied to you,' she stormed, 'is about as appropriate as calling a tiger pussy! I want to go home!'

'And so you shall, *matushka*, in the morning.'

Instantly, wildly, she felt like grabbing at the wheel and forcing him to stop the car, but in that moment a long and laden trailer came towards them out of the night and passed them on the road with a roar that set Chrys's nerves humming like the steel-threads of a violin wound too tightly to take the assault on them.

'Will it make you happy,' she said tautly, 'to make me hate you?'

'I promise you won't hate me, *petite*. What lies ahead of you will be a revelation ... an experience so

68

enjoyable that you will thank me for bringing you to Kent instead of taking you home to prosaic Kensington.'

'You—you actually expect me to *enjoy* myself?' Chrys was almost stunned by the sheer amorality of the man ... the astounding confidence in his own powers of seduction. 'It might come as a surprise to you, *milor*, but there are some girls around who enjoy being—good.'

'Chaste is the word, Miss Devrel. A Victorian, not much used term, these days, and related to the chastity-belt and the blush.'

'With men like you around the chastity-belt should be brought into fashion,' she said frigidly.

'You give me credit for not a single virtue, eh? I am all darkness and devilry in your eyes, is that so?'

'Yes! I knew it from the first moment I laid eyes on you. That man, I said to Dove, likes to make fools of women!'

'How flattering! And would you like to know my thoughts of you?'

'No, thank you!'

'Ah, but you would! You clamour to know even as you make your denial. My immediate thoughts upon recognising you as a dancer I had seen at the Bolshoi were that you had an aura of coolness like that of a fountain in a Moorish patio. That you were white-skinned as the *houri* dreamed of by the Arab in his enclosed garden ... but disdainful of men as the she-tiger who rejects affection as if it were a thorn in her throat. I knew by the candour of your blue eyes that no man had yet made you his mistress ... I knew from

69

the shape of your lips that you were passionate but fastidious.'

'Please, don't stop there,' she said sarcastically. 'I am sure you must have guessed the colour of my lingerie and the location of the tiny mole on my shoulder-blade.'

'*Tu es très charmante*,' he drawled. 'I cannot wait to see this mole on the shoulder-blade.'

'You will be lucky, *milor*. It will be over my dead body.'

'What a pity! You intend, then, to fight to your last breath for your honour?'

'I—I'd put up a pretty good fight.' She flung a look at him, a wing of hair windblown across her face. 'You are taunting me, of course? You don't really intend to take me to Kent?'

'We are now in the county of Kent, *matushka*. Can't you smell the apples in the orchards? It reminds me of certain parts of Russia ... that was why ... yes, this is Kent, and we are on our way to an apartment overlooking the Bay of Sandwich.'

'Oh—you are being monstrous and taking glory in being so! How dare you do this to me?'

'What am I doing to you when my hands are entirely occupied with the wheel of the car?'

'You are taking me somewhere in Kent where I don't want to go! And you imagine that when you get me there I shall suddenly be overcome by your masculine charms and swoon in your arms!'

'Ah, what an attractive image. *Ravissante!*' And very deliberately he quickened the pace of the car, as if he couldn't wait to arrive at his retreat by the sea. Chrys felt furious with him, and curiously defenceless. This kind of situation had never arisen in her life before and she didn't know how to deal with the matter. She was utterly at a loss, for each thing she said was outrageously capped by him, and the only resort would be an undignified tussle with him. Could she, if driven to it, claw with her fingernails at those shockingly beautiful eyes, grey and smouldering as the smoke of a desert fire?

'In the old days,' he drawled, 'they called this kind of thing a Cossack abduction, with the man snatching the girl away on the back of his horse and riding full tilt across the *steppes* with her. After that, of course, she was obliged to marry him, or be labelled a good-time girl to be had by any man who fancied her.'

'And is this the modern variation?' Chrys demanded.

'What do you think, *matushka*?'

'I—I think you've got a nerve! I wouldn't marry you if marriage was bliss and every other man already had a wife! I'd sooner be on the shelf until I'm eighty! I'd sooner emigrate!'

'There is something so passionate about a woman's anger that it really excites a man, so beware of such anger, *matushka*. If I dared to look at your eyes as I drive through this dark old village, I should see them blazing like sapphires. It is fine for a woman to hate— the sabre cut is her indifference.'

'You would know, of course, Prince Anton, being such an authority on the subject. When did you decide to "abduct" me? When you found out I had only a sister and not a brother to put another bullet through that philandering heart of yours?'

'Ah, but don't you care at all that it was very painful for me? I almost died, so you might spare a little

71

sympathy for me. After all, I only went to the silly
girl's bedroom in Monaco to give her the necklace she
lost at the casino. I suppose, looking back, it was a little
absurd of me to go by way of her balcony, but I wished
to spare her the embarrassment of telling her strange,
wild brother that she had been gambling. She was so
delighted to receive her property that she flung her
arms around my neck and kissed me ... at which point
the brother entered the room and shot me. He must
have dragged me on to the balcony, for when the police
came, and the ambulance, he said I was a prowler.
Later it was established who I was, and people pre-
sumed that I was the girl's lover.'

'But didn't she tell the truth—explain the real
facts?' Strangely enough Chrys didn't doubt the vera-
city of his story; she had always sensed that a man so
worldly would so arrange his *amours* that an irate
brother was unlikely to come stalking in on the scene.
There was a secretive side to Prince Anton de Casenove; in his veins ran the instincts of men of power
who had kept concealed in hunting lodges and tower
apartments the *femme chic* of the moment. Swinging
a leg over a balcony in search of love was not in tune
with the suavity and self-assurance of the prince. He
had an aura of sophistication in which boyish escap-
ades played no part ... Chrys felt quite certain that it
had never been part of his plan to be caught returning
the girl's necklace.

'It suited Mademoiselle to let it be thought that I
was in her bedroom in order to be her lover.'

'Oh!'

'She thought I would be honour bound to marry
her.'

'But you aren't all that particular about a girl's honour?'

'Not that of a rather silly blonde with a mad brother.'

'I see.' Chrys's lips formed an involuntary smile. 'It's rather like a stage farce.'

'Except that I have a very realistic scar. Would you care to see it?'

'No——' Chrys bit her lip and her smile was gone, wiped away as she remembered her own precarious position, miles from home, with no one at all to know that she was alone like this with a secretive, amorous, self-willed man who was accustomed to having his own way. 'Please—can't we go back?'

'It is too late for that—see, there is the Bay and the dark gleam of the ocean against the pale sands.'

It was true! She could see the thrust of the cliffs encircling the bay, and she could smell the ocean, and ahead of them, rising against the starlit sky the enormous, almost fearsome bulk of a castle! She stared in sheer amazement at the turrets and round towers as they drew nearer and nearer, and the car swept in through a gateway into the drive of the castle. Gravel crunched beneath the wheels, and lamplight shone in the arched entrances to the towered, grey-walled, romantic residence!

'This is *it*?' she gasped.

'Of course.' He brought the car to a smooth halt in front of a massive corner tower, with narrow windows deepset in the stone, with lights burning softly behind them. 'Did you imagine I had brought you here on a sightseeing tour?'

'But it's a castle!' She stared around her at the

courtyard, and felt the mystery that haunts the environs of an ancient building. Looking upwards, she saw the indented parapets and the thick curtains of ivy mantling the walls. 'Why have we stopped here?'

'For the past couple of hours you have been quite certain of my motive in bringing you all this way.' He slid from the car as he spoke and came round to open the door beside Chrys. 'Come, it is surely traditional for Cinderella to return to the castle after attending the dance.'

'I'm staying right here——'

'No, Chrysdova, you are coming into the castle with me.' His hands were lean and powerful and utterly determined to overrule her defiance. He almost lifted her from the Rapier, and for a brief and electrical moment she was even closer to him than she had been when they had danced together, the silver silk of her dress shining against the darkness of his topcoat, her slim body pressed to him, wild with the instinct of his strength and his potent male grace.

'Please—be reasonable, Anton! Stop playing the villain!'

'Ah, but villains have a better time of it, *chérie*, than men of virtue.' Suddenly he bent his head and kissed her throat, and then, while she still seethed with fury, he marched her into the tower entrance and up a shallow flight of stone steps to an oval-shaped wooden door. He gripped her wrist with one hand, forcibly, actually hurting her, while with the other he inserted a key into the lock of the door and swept it open to a lighted vestibule.

'Well,' he drawled, 'is it so surprising for someone

74

to have an apartment in a centuries-old castle over-looking a smuggler's bay?'

Chrys could only look at him with blazing blue eyes and hate him for his wicked laughter as he pulled her inside the tower and slammed the door behind them.

CHAPTER FIVE

'I SUPPOSE now you're happy?' she stormed.

'Unimaginably. And now will you enter the *petit salon*?' He opened an interior door of the apartment and stood aside for Chrys to enter. She did so unwillingly, knowing that if she had made a dash for the front door he would have been there ahead of her, to bar the way with mocking ease and the assurance that she was in a strange place and in his hands.

Head held high and with a blaze to her eyes, she walked into the *petit salon*, as he had called it, and found herself in a long, shadowy, sensuous room, with several leopardskins stretched on the floor, oddly wrought lamps hanging from the ceiling, dim mirrors, low tables, and divans heaped with cushions. Lamp-shades and curtains blended in dark jewel colours, small fine ornaments stood on various shelves, and there were portraits with penetrating eyes—the family de Casenove eyes!

She spun to face him, with a snarling leopard head at her feet, the velvety pelt under her shoes. 'And now what?' she demanded.

'Oh, surely your outrageous imagination can supply

the answer to that question,' he drawled. He came towards her, silent and lithe as the animal beneath her feet would have walked through the jungle, and with a gleam to his eyes that was equally leopard-like. She backed away, into a divan that caught her behind the knees and tipped her among cushions. She lay there for a few breathless seconds, staring at him, then she twisted to her feet out of his reach.

'*Mon coeur!*'

It was a woman's voice, and Chrys swung round to see that a woman had appeared from a curtained doorway, to stand there outlined against the topaz velvet. She wore a kaftan of deep-purple brocade, trimmed with braid around the full sleeves, and she was gazing at Prince Anton with radiant dark eyes set in a high-boned, Slavonic face that was neither old nor young, but had a curious agelessness about it. Her hair was covered by a kind of veil, almost nun-like, and as she stretched her arms towards Anton, they made the graceful speaking movements that a ballet dancer never loses her whole life through.

'*Dushechka!*' He strode past Chrys towards the woman, and with a loving hunger he wrapped her in his arms and kissed her face for several moments.

'You are so unpredictable,' laughed the woman. 'To come at this hour—and driving, of course, like a hare through the night!'

'Of course, *tu*.'

'Just to see me?'

'Is there another woman whose charm can reach out like yours to a man?'

'Even yet, Anton?' The woman pressed her hand to his heart and studied his downbent, quizzical face.

There was something poignant in her gesture, as if she still believed that he might suffer or die of his injury ... and it was in that moment that the truth struck at Chrys.

It struck even as Anton de Casenove turned to her, his left arm still encircling the woman he had greeted so affectionately.

'Miss Devrel, I played a trick on you, but only because you seemed so certain I was abducting you. But all I really wanted was for an English dancer to meet a Russian one. Won't you come and meet Miroslava?'

Chrys had imagined his grandmother miles away in her desert house ... not for one second during that drive had she dreamed that he was really bringing her to see the woman who had fled during a revolution and borne a son to a murdered prince. A son who in his turn had died in uniform.

Seeing her, and the way she touched Anton as if to make sure he lived and breathed and was not lost to her like the other men she had loved, Chrys could understand why she had taught him from a boy to live his life to the full.

To taste the wine of every experience in case the cup was snatched from his lips while he was still a young man!

She approached Miroslava and held out her hand with a smile. 'I'm thrilled, *madame*, to meet a ballerina who danced for kings. I can only imagine how exciting it must have been in the days when dashing officers actually drank wine from the slippers of their favourites of the ballet. Prince Anton tells me that you were a great favourite.'

'So you are a dancer?' The appraisal of the dark

slanting eyes was rapid and expert, taking in the pure modelling of Chrys's face, and the slim suppleness of her body in the silver dress. 'And no man has yet enjoyed his wine from your slipper, *hein?*'

Chrys smiled involuntarily, and felt almost at once that fine steely thread of communication which exists between people of the same profession who love it with the same nervous intensity. 'The outward trappings of ballet have become very prosaic since your exciting days, *madame.*'

'And you wish you could have known them, eh? The stage deep in flowers at the end of a performance, and *troikas* unharnessed from the horses so that handsome, crazy Guardsmen could pull them through the streets, with the ballerinas laughing among Serbian furs like pampered dolls, and often flourishing a whip over the broad shoulders. Yes, crazy, exciting days, never to be known again.'

Miroslava glanced up at her grandson. 'So when you telephoned this morning, *rouh*, this is what you meant by saying you could bring me a surprise?'

'And do you like your surprise, *dushechka?*' He quirked an eyebrow. 'I personally thought it too good an opportunity to miss, to bring you a young ballerina who lives for nothing but her art, but who must give it up for a year to enable her spine to fully heal after a bad accident. I thought that you alone could assure her that once a dancer always a dancer. Miss Devrel fears that her career will suffer if she is forced to discontinue her ballet dancing, but I feel sure you can convince her that to learn other aspects of life during that year will be of immense value to her as an artiste.'

'My child, you have my sympathy.' The dark eyes

78

of Miroslava were instantly compassionate. 'Yes, now I look at you I see in your face a fine-drawn look of recent suffering, and in your eyes a fear of the future. Anton and I between us must dispel for you the anxiety—but first of all I must know your first name. We Slavs love diminutives and titles, but we dislike formality. I cannot call you *Miss*.'

'I am called Chrys.'

'Chris—like a boy?' The arching of the dark brow was very reminiscent of the grandson.

'Chrys—golden flower,' Anton broke in smoothly. 'And now let me take your wrap, *matushka*.' He did so, sliding it from her shoulders and making her aware of his tallness behind her, his fingertips brushing her bare arms and leaving, it seemed, a trail of fire in their wake. What was his game? Was he genuinely concerned that she learn from Miroslava that her career could be gripped by both hands and held on to despite this setback? Or was he playing some devious role of his own—his ultimate aim to subdue her resistance to him?

'Perhaps, *Grand'mère*, Vera could make us some tea and provide a snack?' he said. 'We had dinner at eight, and the drive was a long one.'

'*Tout de suite*,' she exclaimed. 'What am I thinking of not to offer refreshment! But this young dancer, she fascinates me because you bring her to see me!' Miroslava clapped her hands, and like a genie a woman appeared from behind the curtained doorway. She had obviously been listening to the conversation and her face was seamed in smiles as she bobbed a curtsey at Anton and spoke to him in Russian. He replied in the same tongue, and because the woman was about the

79

same age as Madame, Chrys realised that she was the maid who had fled from Russia with her mistress all those years ago and had been with her ever since.

'Do come and sit down.' Madame drew Chrys to a divan beneath one of the Moorish ceiling lamps, and everything felt so strange and foreign to her as she sat down beside Miroslava and saw the filigreed bracelets piled on to the fragile wrists, and the gleam of henna on the long narrow fingertips. Madame also wore an Eastern perfume, exotic as the slant to her eyes and the tiny mole at the corner of her mouth.

There was power in her, and the magnetism which her grandson had inherited. The drive of a 'girl of the people' who had married a prince in secret and lived many years with the memory of his love.

Miroslava was still a woman to reckon with ... to hold spellbound strong and wilful men ... she was exciting, and must have been wonderful as a young woman when her golden-tinted skin was unlined and her eyes filled with the fire of her youth and her passion.

Chrys could understand why Anton de Casenove adored his grandmother; not only had she been his 'parent' and his mentor, but she had a rich personality, a wealth of feeling in her heart, and that insidious charm of the woman who had lived fully and without a single regret.

'These two children wish for supper,' she called over her shoulder to her maid Vera. And then prepare the *pussinka* a room for the night. Antonyi can sleep on a divan here in the *petit salon*, and he can cover himself with the fur laprobe which covered me and my coming child when I fled from the revolutionaries.'

'You are indomitable, my darling grandmother, and will always be so.' He bent over her hand and kissed the hennaed fingers with casual grace. 'I wanted Chrysdova to meet a woman who was also forced to give up something which she loved with all her heart. Two things, eh? Your dancing and your husband, with whom you would have stayed but for the child.'

'Ivanyi would not leave,' she said sadly, 'but for the sake of his son—I knew from the first moment of knowing that I should have a son—I left him to be killed by the mob. When his son was born, many miles from Russia but beneath an Eastern sky, I developed some trouble in my left leg and was never able to dance again as a ballerina. These things seem like a punishment at the time, and you search your mind and your heart for the reason.'

Miroslava paused and gave Chrys a long, intent look. 'It could be, my child, that you must learn other facets of living before going on with your career. Art is wonderful, but not to make of it a bondage. Great dancers have done so and it has killed them before their time. Pavlova lived only to dance and she sacrificed the passionate reality of her own being so that her Dying Swan could be immortal. It was wonderful to see her, with her dark head bound in the pale swan's feathers, and her limbs as graceful as the swan's neck —but there was an element of tragedy in her performance that could break your heart. Day by day, hour by hour, she had given herself to the dance—her very soul.'

Miroslava made an eloquent gesture with her speaking hands. 'To be a Slav is to have a love of suffering. The Russian soul, *l'âme slave*. But even so I would sooner sacrifice myself for another human being. The perfection of love can be the greatest art of all, but alas too few people take the trouble to perfect the art of love.'

'Chrysdova has forsworn love.' Anton had made himself comfortable on a divan, stretched full length and relaxed as a dark, sleek cat of the jungle. His eyes dwelt lazily on Chrys, such a fair contrast to his grandmother and himself. 'She dreams only of being a ballerina, and is in agony at being parted from the torments of the *barre* and the *pointe*. What strange, complex creatures women are; almost less fond of the creature comforts than the male of the species.'

'You see and hear speaking a male creature who very much likes his comforts,' said Madame, drily. 'That is when he is in Europe, for the real fact of the matter, Chrysdova, is that he has two sides to him. I have known him endure and exult in the most trying desert conditions, just like *l'arabe*. Though to see him at the moment one would think him terribly lazy and luxury loving.'

Chrys smiled and gave him a swift look that avoided a meeting with his eyes, which she knew to be glinting in the lamplight, like a kind of gem made up of fascinating shades of grey. It flashed across her mind yet again that no man had the right to possess such wickedly marvellous eyes, with the added deceit of double black lashes. Such eyes could conceal a thousand wicked thoughts.

'Are you on a visit to England, *madame*?' Chrys asked. 'I know from what your grandson has told me that you have a house in the East, with the fascinating name of *Belle Tigresse*.'

'So Anton has told you about the house, eh? It used to be my desert abode, but now it belongs to him. I grow old, *pussinka*, and the climate of the East is no longer good for me, or my faithful Vera. Ah, how the years have quickly passed, and yet they were filled with incident! Vera and I have settled here in Kent, with its apple orchards which remind me of the Russia of my girlhood. Did Anton not tell you that he was bringing you to see his grandmother?'

'No, *madame*.' Chrys shot him a severe look. 'He behaved disgracefully and let me assume that he was— abducting me.'

'Like a Cossack, eh?' Miroslava laughed with great enjoyment. 'Anton is so like his grandfather—look, there on the mantel! There is a photograph of Ivanyi.'

Chrys arose from the divan with her own particular grace, and knew herself watched by the grandson as she took into her hands the silver-framed photograph of the dead prince. He wore a superb white uniform embroidered with an eagle, gauntlets on his hands, a sword in his hilt, leather kneeboots, and a fur-trimmed hat. On a less handsome man the uniform would have been fabulous, but Prince Ivanyi had a distinction, a dashing air of a man who took what he could not beguile from the ladies. The eyes ... Chrys didn't need to turn her head to compare the pictured eyes with those she could feel almost tangibly on her person.

'In the twin frame,' said Miroslava, 'there is a picture of myself as a girl ... a girl who danced on the very air in those far-off, legendary days of the Maryinsky, of snow-capped towers, and jingling *troikas*. It was all really true, and yet now like a dream.'

Chrys gazed with wonderment at the vivid, eloquent

face of the young Miroslava, wearing a black off-the-shoulder dress, with full sleeves, a satin bodice, and a flared chiffon skirt.

'That was when I danced the *pas de deux* of Siegfried and Odile.' There was nostalgia, and a note of husky longing in the deep voice of the woman who had known great happiness and deep sorrow. 'Ivanyi always liked the costume, and that particular role for me. He always said I was too passionate to be a heroine. He knew me well, did my dark huntsman, my Orion, like a star that burned with too much flame for long living. I was his black swan, and always he was my dark huntsman ... not always a kind or forgiving man, but irresistible as honey to the bee, as flame to the moth. I would live again those two years that were my lovetime and not regret a single one of them.'

Chrys felt a slight tremor in her hand as she replaced the photograph on the shelf. Never had her own family spoken with such frankness of their personal feelings ... the love between her parents had always seemed a gentle, patient, tolerant emotion, binding them closely like the pattern of a durable carpet. She had never thought of their love as being like a flame, and she knew instinctively that it never had been. Their love was made to wear, to endure ... but now she read in Miroslava's eyes the story of another kind of love.

She was glad that Vera entered the room in that moment, wheeling before her a trolley on which stood a lovely old samovar of silver, tea-glasses in filigreed containers, and plates of sandwiches.

'Food!' exclaimed Anton, as if he had not eaten for hours. In a single supple movement he was on his feet and bending over the trolley. 'What have we here, Vera? Smoked salmon, I hope?'

'Have you not always loved it, *barin*?' smiled Vera, addressing him as the 'master' but looking at him as if she still thought of him as the wild boy who had been delivered into the care of his grandmother by the elopement of his mother.

Chrys found it difficult to picture him as a boy, and when Miroslava talked of him as *l'arabe*, yet another side of this worldly, well-dressed, cynical man-about-town came into focus to confuse her still further. She was beginning to wonder which was the real Anton de Casenove. Last night he had appeared wholly as a rake who chased after women ... tonight she learned that his motive in being in that French girl's bedroom had not been an amorous one at all but a recklessly gallant one.

Watching him with Miroslava now convinced Chrys that he cared for no other woman on this earth but Madame. She alone held the key to his sardonic personality. She alone knew what inner devil drove him to the gaming tables of Europe; on bold safaris through the drawing-rooms of the *beau monde*, charming his way into the hearts of women but never offering a single proposal of marriage.

Was it possible that he reaped a sort of revenge on his mother by making women love him, only to laugh at them as he flung himself into the saddle of a swift horse and galloped the aroma of their perfume out of his nostrils?

Seen in this light he was even more dangerous. A rake was forgivable, for he loved women too well. Anton de Casenove didn't love women at all. To him

they were all as faithless as his mother had been ...
that gay and reckless mother who had run off and left
his father to die in the war.

Chrys watched him as his fine teeth flashed in a smile
and his dark head almost touched the jade tassels on
the Moorish ceiling lamps. The silver samovar purred
as the tea-glasses were filled from the little tap at the
side of the urn.

The scene was cosy enough, but the feelings that
smouldered beneath the surface were those of people
strange to Chrys, and with an intense emotionalism
bred in their very bones. They hated ... or they loved
... in equal fiery measure. There was little of the
gentleness which Chrys had witnessed in the lives of
her parents; and in the romance between Dove and
Jeremy.

Anton brought her a glass of tea and as he placed
the filigreed container in her hand, his eyes looked
down into hers. She almost shrank away from him
among the cushions of the divan ... she didn't believe
for one moment that he cared about her career as a
dancer, her future, or her feelings.

'You will have some sandwiches?' he asked, and
there was no doubt about the thread of mockery that
ran through his words, as if he had noticed her with-
drawal from him, her avoidance of his fingers as she
took the glass of tea. 'You must be feeling a few
twinges of hunger after that long drive into the
country?'

He knew that whatever twinges she felt were in no
way connected with hunger. He knew far too much
about women and the workings of their minds and

their hearts ... he played on that knowledge and used it to make fools of women.

Well, thought Chrys, the time had come to show him what one female thought of him and his penchant for tearing the pride off women as a naughty boy might tear the wings off pretty moths.

Chrys met his look and quite deliberately she let her blue eyes fill with coldness and dislike. Blue eyes, she had once been told by a ballet teacher, could look as chilling as they could look heavenly, and she knew she conveyed a cold disdain to Anton when he shrugged his wide shoulders and walked away from her.

She turned with a smile to Vera. 'Yes, please, I will have a couple of those delicious-looking sandwiches.'

'Something,' drawled Anton, 'has put an edge on Miss Devrel's tongue.'

'Our Kentish air, perhaps,' said Miroslava.

But as Chrys drank her tea and ate her sandwiches, she could feel Madame studying her profile with reflective eyes. What was she thinking, that it was unusual for a girl to be so cool towards her grandson.

'So what will you do, *pussinka*, during this year when you must "rest" from your dancing?' Miroslava asked her.

'I—might travel.' It was then that she made up her mind on this issue which Dove had raised. 'I don't like the idea of working in an office, nor do I think I'd be much good at it, so I shall loan myself out as a travelling companion. My sister knows someone who is going abroad very soon, and if I am not in the vicinity of theatres and the people I know in ballet, then I might avoid the temptation to return to the stage before it is wise for me to do so.'

'So you have decided to spend twelve long months with the "dotty aunt", eh? Are you not afraid that she will send you dotty?' The words were interposed with such suavity from the occupant of the other divan that Chrys was wildly tempted to aim a cushion at his head.

'Ignore him,' smiled Madame, 'and tell me to which part of the world you expect to travel.'

'Somewhere in the East, I think. Anyway, I must first persuade my sister's fiancé's aunt that I'm capable of making a good companion.' Chrys smiled a little, and kept her gaze from that other divan. 'I've always been so independent, and I've heard that companions are rather at the beck and call of their employers.'

'I am sure you will cope admirably, *pussinka*. Ballet teaches one the art of patience even as it portrays the most emotional aspects of life, such as desire, suffering, and love. A great *maître de ballet*, who was himself a Russian, once said to me long ago that a dancer can be anything that she chooses to be, a sword, a chalice, or a rose. You will be very patient, Chrysdova, and enjoy your travels, and prepare yourself to return to dancing with a fine strong backbone again.'

'My fear is that I shall be less of a dancer.' Chrys sighed. 'I worked so hard to become a soloist, and there are so many young and talented dancers ready to step into your shoes. It was such a bad stroke of luck to have that fall ...'

'These things, my child, are sent to test our strength of character.' Miroslava took her hand, the left one, and gazed into the palm of it. 'You have a long life-line, Chrysdova, so there is plenty of time for you to become the ballerina of your dreams. But tell me, have you no other dreams?'

88

'Of romance?' Chrys spoke a trifle scornfully, and was very much aware that Anton was listening with arrogant laziness to their conversation. 'It was something I never allowed to interfere with my career.'

'But we must all be madly in love just once in a lifetime,' said Miroslava whimsically, while her rings pressed into the slenderness of Chrys's hand. 'Art has an imperious voice, but love has a seductive one. When you hear it——'

'No,' Chrys broke in. 'I don't intend to hear it, or to listen to its unreason. So few marriages survive the career of the wife; so many obstacles are put in her way that her career is sacrificed. Perhaps I'm selfish——'

'No.' Miroslava spoke firmly. 'You have not the lips that express self-love and self-interest alone. There is a fine sensitivity to their outline, which means you are capable of *stradan*. The selfish are incapable of this in its acutest sense.'

'*Stradan*.' Chrys murmured the Russian word for suffering, even as she recalled with a shudder that crashing fall and the pain like claws in her spine. Yet it wasn't this kind of suffering which the word signified; it went deeper and embodied the soul of a person. *L'âme slave*. It meant that she was complicated, self-tormenting as these people with whom she drank Russian tea.

'Yes, it is all there, the temperament of the artiste.' Miroslava patted her hand and smiled in her worldly way tempered by her warmth of heart. 'Rebellion, and innocence, with a dash of cynicism learned on the ladder to solo dancing. The cast-iron fragility. The determination that you need no one—no one but yourself to reach the stars. *Pussinka*, do you think I don't know? But I also know that when love came along with its voice like no other voice I had to listen. You too——'

'No!' Again Chrys shook her head. 'I'm not like my sister. She longs for the chains——'

'Chains, you call them?'

'Can you deny that they aren't?' Chrys looked steadily at the Russian woman who had loved, and borne a child, and found herself finished as a dancer because of love's chains.

'Velvet chains, perhaps.' Miroslava looked deeply into Chrys's blue eyes. 'This coming year will be your testing time, Chrysdova. If you come through it without an entanglement, then you will become the mistress of the dance instead of the wife of a man. I predict this—but I also say to you—beware! We have the choice to begin love, but not always to end it. If we slay it, then we pay with the coin of loneliness.'

'It's a chance I'm willing to take,' said Chrys, with the bravado of her youth, and the untroubled coolness of the girl who only felt fully alive when she danced. She was confident, sitting there in the firelight of Miroslava's castle room, with the lamplight gleaming softly on her fair hair. She even dared to look at Anton de Casenove, who reclined at his ease, with his dark head against a cushion, and a cheroot between his lips. His eyelids drooped over his grey eyes, so the lashes concealed their expression. He didn't speak, and yet he seemed to challenge her statement with that lazy look.

'I mean it,' she said. 'It won't bother me to be a bachelor girl.'

'But it might bother the bachelors.' Miroslava glanced at her grandson. 'Do you find Chrysdova a pretty creature, *mon ami*?'

'She is an ice-witch left by the frost when it sculptures its way across the *steppes*,' he drawled. 'If the *matushka* goes to the East then she might be in danger of melting a little in that ardent sunlight. A rich sheik might see her and snatch her for his *harem*—see, Miroslava, how scornful she looks! She doesn't yet know that the East is the most unchanging place left on earth, where *harems* still exist within secluded courts to which no man is admitted except the sheik himself.'

'Nothing is decided,' said Chrys, who didn't argue with him about his own knowledge of the ardent side of Eastern life. 'I may not suit as a companion, so then it will mean a nine-to-five job in a city office.'

'Most unexciting,' he rejoined, 'and most unlikely for you. I think the desert is on the cards for you ... *le destin*.'

'Which is all very well,' said Madame, 'but we will not get ourselves involved in a discussion about destiny at this time of the night. Look at Chrysdova! She has the look of a child who is trying hard to keep her eyes from closing, and I am an old woman who needs her dreams. No doubt, *mon ami*, you are well used to staying awake all night at the card table, not to mention your night riding in the desert.'

'Talk not of things desired and distant as the stars,' he jested, rising to his feet, tall in the lamplight, which cast strange shadows across the distinction and the devilry of his lean face. Chrys could imagine him both as a gambler, and a desert rider, a cloak billowing out from those wide shoulders like the wings of a hawk.

He came to Miroslava and assisted her to her feet, and he held her frail but still graceful figure close to him for a moment. 'I owe to you, *dushechka*, the good that is in me. But remember also what you taught me when I was a boy. "Make yourself a lamb and the wolf will eat you." Come, do you recall that you said it to me?'

She laughed a little and pressed her cheek against his dark jacket. 'I remember, and I would have you no different, son of my son.'

He bent his head and kissed his grandmother's forehead, and as he did so his eyes flicked across the face of Chrys, as if he were curious about her reaction to his affection for Miroslava. She was caught by his eyes, held by his gaze, and she saw deep in his eyes laughter like a tiny flame. She knew he laughed at her because she had believed he meant to seduce her ... it was awful that he should know her thoughts ... mortifying that he should be in a position to be amused by her naïvety.

Chrys jumped to her feet. 'I am ready for bed,' she said, and instantly the dark eyebrow was peaking above the grey eyes, and her cheeks flamed as she realised how he interpreted her remark. His pleasure in her confusion was diabolical, and she only wished that she might get her own back with him.

But tomorrow they would part ... she to go and see this aunt of Jeremy's ... he to ride, or play cards, or find some other woman to tease.

'Come,' said Miroslava, taking her arm. 'I will show you to your room.'

'*Bonsoir*, Miss Devrel,' drawled the prince.

'Goodnight, *m'sieur*,' she replied, and was glad to escape from his mocking face, his lean elegance, his slightly sadistic treatment of all women but Miroslava.

A little winding staircase led to her bedroom. A secret stairway in days gone by, she was told. 'A lover's stairway, perhaps,' murmured Miroslava, as she led

Chrys into a turret bedroom, with cupboards deep in the walls, bowed glass windows, and an icon affixed to the wall, with a silver lamp lighting it.

'Sleep well, *pussinka moiya*.' Miroslava patted Chrys's cheek, pale now the flush had left it. 'I am pleased that Anton brought you to see me. On the bed you will find a nightdress and a robe, and the bathroom is at the turn of the corridor. You will be all right?'

'I shall be fine, *madame*. You have been very kind to me.'

'Kinder than Anton, eh?' There was a knowing gleam in the dark eyes that regarded Chrys by the soft light of the lamp. 'He is not like other men you have met, I think. He is subtle, and appears to say what is in his mind without really saying it at all, which I know can be very confusing and infuriating for a woman. Ivanyi was the same, and in the way of heredity Anton is so much like him. The same pride and self-will; same daring and defiance of the conventions laid down by others. When I first met Ivanyi I was a little terrified, but I was also a Tartar and so I fought with him every inch of the way into love.'

Miroslava smiled a little, and moved her hands in a very foreign way. 'Destiny does weave the pattern of one's life, and it will be intriguing, eh, if you should meet Anton again in surroundings a little wilder than the apple orchards of Kent? Had you thought that this might happen, if you go East with this woman as her companion?'

'I don't want to meet him——' Chrys bit her lip. 'What I mean to say, *madame*, is that Prince Anton and I have nothing in common, not really, although I found him a marvellous dancer. It would be better if we didn't see each other again——'

'Safer, do you mean?' Miroslava gave a soft laugh and turned to the door. 'Be warned, *pussinka*, that if you play for safety you will find the game of life a rather dull one. It may be what you want, to be safe, but it will be such a waste. *Bon soir*, Chrysdova. Sleep and dream.'

'Goodnight, *madame*, and thank you again for your kindness to me.'

'Your blue eyes invite kindness, my child, but I speak as a woman.' Miroslava again laughed softly as she closed the door of the bedroom behind her, and like her grandson left a subtle insinuation in the air that was faintly perfumed by the oil that burned in the *lampada*.

Chrys breathed it, and it seemed redolent of the distant East ... a strange and beckoning scent, like that of hidden courtyards and jasmine gardens.

Her pulses quickened ... she would go tomorrow and see the woman who desired a companion for her travels in the East. It was a vast place and her path might never cross again the path of Anton de Casenove.

But if it did ...? The question stole into her mind and played there like an imp of the devil. She wondered what she would do, and gazed as if for future protection at the wall icon lit by the silver lamp.

There was, however, one thing she was very sure of ... Dove must be dissuaded from inviting the prince to her wedding. Chrys had made up her mind that when she parted from him the following day, the parting would be as definite as she could make it.

It would be a goodbye, not *do svidania*!

CHAPTER SIX

IT was a wonderful old tree, rich with foliage and with a broad trunk which had divided to form almost the shape of a heart, as depicted on playing cards. So ancient was the tree that the names carved upon it dated back to Norman times and the tribulations of lovers at the cruel courts of the old kings.

Chrys had woken early in the bedroom with the cool pale walls and the golden icon, and not hearing a sound from the other rooms she glanced from the window near her bed, and the old tree on the lawn below seemed to beckon to her. She decided at once to take a stroll round the castle grounds, and after taking a shower she slipped into the white shantung dress which Vera had brought to her last night, with the kind suggestion that she might have need of it. It was delightfully reminiscent of the Thirties, and the sleeveless jacket in crochet-work reached to Chrys's hips. She loved the outfit, and could hardly appear in daylight in a silver dance dress. Such an apparition on the lawn might be taken for a ghost in the early morning mist.

Mist in the morning at this time of the year was invariably a sign of a glorious day to come, and as Chrys wandered about the velvet lawns, she breathed the drifting sea air and felt rather like a very young girl on holiday again. She was hungry for a large breakfast, and felt a longing to drive to the edge of the sea and to swim in the joyous water.

She paused where a thick cluster of honeysuckle covered a grey stone wall and she had a feeling that Miroslava and her grandson would expect her to stay for the day. She touched the flowers, and the dew was on her fingertips and she wondered if she would be wise to surrender to this holiday feeling; to stay a while longer in the dangerous company of Anton de Casenove. He had a flair for making life exciting and expectant, and Chrys knew that she ought not to yield to the charming peril of the man.

She wanted above all to remain the well-balanced dancer, admired for her coolness and the way she had of keeping the men at bay. She wanted to dance in the cool halls of career, without the turmoil of desire in her life.

She was old enough, and woman enough, to have felt it tingling in her veins when she had danced in his arms last night. He would have that effect on anyone, and it would be sheer madness to fall in love with him.

She stroked the honeysuckle and the soft salty air stroked the skin of her arms and her neck and moved her hair with its caress. She tilted her chin. Was she such an innocent that she had to run away in order to protect herself from a mere man? If she returned to London today it would be to an empty flat. Dove would be at work, and after cooking her lunch there would be little for Chrys to do, except to go and see a film or sit in the park with a book.

No, she wouldn't run away! If Miroslava asked her to stay here in Kent for the day she would do so, and take Anton's attentions for what they really were, a mixture of charm and deliberate enticement, with not a bit of heart behind them.

With a smile on her lips she returned across the lawn, which was now fingered by the sun that was breaking golden and bright through the mist that veiled the blue sky. She entered the archway that led to the winding stairs and upwards to Miroslava's apartment. Suddenly she gave a gasp as someone came round the curve of the narrow stairway—long-legged, wearing a white shirt open at the throat, and a sardonic smile about his lips.

'*Bonjour*,' he greeted her. 'You are an early riser—though we did wonder if you had taken fright and plunged off in search of the nearest railway depot.'

'*Bonjour, milor*.' She gave him a smile that hid a certain turbulence of her nerves. He mustn't know that she had thought of making a bolt for it; he was the type who liked too much to give chase. 'I looked from my window and saw that grand old tree on the lawn and just had to go and read the initials. So strange and sad, somehow, that they still linger while the owners of them have long since gone to dust.'

'You are a romantic, Chrysdova, though you delight in denying it. I have come to fetch you to the breakfast table, and I hope you have an enormous appetite, because Vera always cooks French-fried potatoes with the ham and eggs when I am staying here with Grand-'mère.'

'I am ravenous,' Chrys admitted. 'It must be the sea air, because I never feel all that hungry in London.'

'Come!' He held out a hand to her, but she ignored it and raced past him, slim enough not to brush too closely against him. But his soft laughter was even more effective than actual contact would have been this early in the morning; it mocked her, and it knew all about

97

her fear of his fascination. It told her in more than words that he was delighted that she wasn't unafraid of him. She bit her lip as she entered the morning-room where Vera was laying the table. She wished to goodness she could be ice-cool with him, and delicately she moved out of the doorway as he entered the room behind her.

Vera turned to give her a smile. 'Ah, I see that the dress fits you, *mademoiselle*, and it looks much nicer on you than it ever did on me. How grand to be young and pretty, eh? On such a day as this will be, and with the *barin* to show you this Kent which Madame and I have grown to love.'

Vera bustled away to bring in the food, and Chrys cast a glance at Anton which couldn't help but reflect her curiosity.

'You are staying.' It was a statement, not a question. 'You are not basically a city girl, so what has the city to offer you on a summer's day? Here we have the orchards and the sea—do you like to bathe?'

'Yes——' The word came to her lips involuntarily. 'But I have no bathing suit, *milor*.'

'That is no problem.' He lounged on the deep window-seat and with his arms stretched at either side of him, the collar of his shirt was thus opened against the smooth brown skin of his throat and chest. Chrys picked up a goblet from the oak sideboard and studied that in order to keep her gaze from the man, who in all conscience was devastatingly good to look at.

'That goblet is a hundred years old,' he informed her. 'It is made from real Bohemian glass and it is for a bride and her groom to drink from on their wedding day. A romantic notion, eh? First he drinks, and then the bride follows suit, and the wine is an old Russian wine which has been blessed. When Miroslava fled from Russia there were few things she could take with her, but the goblet she could not leave behind. She wrapped it in her chemise so it would not get broken— hold it to the light and see it sparkle like a ruby.'

Chrys obeyed him and caught her breath at the beauty of the thing, perfectly oval and balanced on a long jewelled stem. 'How gorgeous are really old things! One can see at once that they are fashioned by dedicated craftsmen and not turned out on a conveyor belt in some high-rise factory with plateglass windows.'

'So you are admiring my second greatest treasure, eh, child?' Madame came into the morning-room at that moment and Chrys nodded and gave her a warm smile.

'What is your other treasure, *madame*? May I be impulsive and ask to see that as well?'

Miroslava chuckled and gestured with a ringed hand at her grandson. 'By all means take a good look, *matushka*. I brought from Russia just two things that meant my very life to me, my marriage goblet and my unborn baby. There stands the son of the child I bore in the desert, who was destined never to know his father. I am grateful to the powers of heaven that Anton knew his own father as a boy. He was a fine man. Anton, of course, is more of a devil, but what woman is proof against a devil who has charm?'

'And what man is proof against Vera and her magical hand with French-fried potatoes?' he smiled, coming to the table as Vera wheeled in the food trolley and pulling out a chair for his grandmother. Chrys replaced the goblet on the sideboard and quickly took her own chair. The sun was now streaming through the lancet windows and making delightful patterns across the lace tablecloth and picking out the silver lights in the cutlery and the toast rack.

'I never partake of a big breakfast,' said Miroslava. 'Toast and coffee are sufficient for me, but I enjoy watching young people at work on good food.'

'We aim to oblige you in every respect, Grand'mère.' Anton broke a roll and helped himself to butter while Chrys was busy helping herself to eggs, slices of gammon with the fat all crinkly, and puffed chips as golden as new pennies.

Vera joined them at the table after she had brought in the coffee, and it was a lighthearted meal, with Madame and her companion full of tales about the old days in Russia. Chrys enjoyed this hour because she felt secure ... it was being alone with Anton that shook her composure and made her feel as unsure of herself as she felt of him.

'You are not returning to London straight away?' Miroslava enquired at Chrys, her dark eyes roving the fair hair of her young guest, lit by the sunlight and softly loose on her shoulders. 'It would be such a pity, for you have no rehearsal to dash to. Why not spend the day with us?'

'With you?' Chrys spoke eagerly. 'Yes, I should enjoy that. You can tell me all about the Russian Imperial ballet ...'

'Ah, but I did not mean for you to stay cooped up indoors.' Miroslava glanced in Anton's direction. 'It will be good for my grandson to have the company of a *nice* girl for the day. You can drive into Applegate and take with you a basket lunch to enjoy on the beach. You can forget ballet for once, *matushka*, and relax in the sun. All work and no play is not good for a pretty girl. It is against nature.'

'But——'

Anton quirked an eyebrow at Chrys. 'But is a word invented by the mule to excuse his obstinacy. You like the seaside, no?'

'Yes,' she admitted. 'But I don't want to bother you by expecting you to take me sightseeing.'

'I assure you it will be no bother.' And as he leaned forward to help himself to marmalade, his eyes looked into hers and held a ray of amused awareness. 'Even nice girls can be quite distracting, and I have nothing else to do.'

A remark which in itself struck her as the height of decadence. *Nice* men worked for a living; they didn't play at cards for money, or gamble on the horses.

'Anton means that he is idle when he is here in Europe,' Miroslava said, as if she had noticed the way Chrys had looked at him, a hint of censure in her blue eyes. 'There is work enough at El Kadir, so don't pretend, Anton, that you are lazy and improvident. I never brought you up to play all the time, now did I? I taught you that play is the reward for hard work, as it is in ballet. Now confess to this girl that you are not a rake, for I believe she has the idea that you are.'

'Confession, this early in the day?' His eyes laughed, and with a swift supple movement he was on his feet, around the table, and on his knees to Chrys—who gazed at him with fascinated blue eyes despite herself. His face seemed to her to be almost frightening in its male beauty, like the golden mask of a tombed prince ... as if indeed there were things buried in his soul which he had kept hidden a long time and would not

101

reveal ... unless like a stroke of lightning love came to him and made him reveal himself.

'Oh, do get up off your knees!' The words broke from her, half-laughingly. 'You make a mock of everything.'

'Better than making a gloom of it, surely?'

'I—I suppose so.' She sat there as tense as a cat confronted by a tiger, aware in all her nerves that he wasn't as playful as he made out to be. 'Well, what do I have to do? Stroke you to make you purr?' she demanded.

'Would you like to stroke me?' His eyes were wickedly amused, and yet a soft, beckoning lambency had crept into them, and she felt her clenched fingers uncurling and the oddest, most maddening urge was creeping through them. To offset this she struck at his shoulder and felt the hard muscle and warmth of him. 'You haven't the frame of a layabout, *milor*.'

'I fence and I ride,' he drawled. 'The pastimes of a rake.'

'True, but if you stay down there on the rug much longer you'll have housemaid's knee, and I understand that it's rather painful.'

He gave a laugh and in one supple movement was standing over her. Then he glanced at Miroslava. 'You see how it is, Grand'mère? The English girl remains elusive and hard to catch because she refuses to surrender her independent right to have a mind and a will of her own. She is the cat that bristles instead of the minx that flatters. She is a challenge, eh?'

'Well?' Miroslava studied Chrys, who sat there with a characteristic tilt to her chin, and the elusive outline of a dimple near her lips. 'Are you pleased to be a

102

challenge to a man who has been wooed by two European princesses, a Romanian countess, and the daughter of one of the richest oil shieks?'

'My unsophistication is the challenge, *madame*. I amuse him—for a day or two.'

'You think so?' Miroslava studied her grandson, and then she changed the subject until breakfast was over and they went into the *salon*, where Madame took a dark Russian cigarette from a box and fitted it into an ivory holder. Anton lit it for her, and then she sat down on a divan and gave a little satisfied sigh. 'You are going to the beach, you two?'

'Of course.' He didn't wait for Chrys to agree or disagree. 'I must bathe in English waters before I make my return to the desert. What a *memoir du coeur*, what coolness to remember under that hot sun—that of the English sea and a girl like Chrysdova. The combination is irresistible.'

'I really think that I should be getting back to London,' Chrys said, in a cool voice. 'My sister will be worried about me——'

'You can telephone to let her know that you are perfectly all right,' he said, and there was a sudden note of iron in his voice, a warning that his mind was made up for her and that she would be unwise to argue with him. 'Come, the phone is in the hall, and while you give Dove a ring I will go and make sure that Vera packs a perfect lunch for us.'

He took her by the wrist and she knew it would be useless to appeal to Miroslava, who sat smoking dreamily, as if the scent of her cigarette awoke memories which she didn't wish to have disturbed. His fingers were like steel about her wrist, and she cast him

103

a furious little glance as he made her go to the phone. 'I suppose,' she said, 'this is how you treat your desert women?'

'Invariably,' he drawled. 'I am always dragging one or the other around by the hair.'

Chrys glanced at him, and when his lip quirked she had to smile herself. 'A harem would bore you, wouldn't it, *milor*? You like to go out and hunt your prey; you don't like tamed birds.'

'The *ennui* of anything tame would be impossible to endure.' He gestured at the telephone on the little round table. 'Go ahead and ring your sister. Tell her you are in perfectly safe hands.'

'You must be joking!' Chrys scoffed. 'You forget that Dove has seen you.'

'You think I am entirely what I appear to be?'

'Aren't you?'

'No more than you, *chérie*.' And lightly, as if to soothe her ruffled feelings, he passed a lean hand over her silky hair. '*Soie sauvage*, a golden banner of your spirit and your courage. You are well named, Chrysdova. Now,' his tone of inflexibility lay under the velvet, 'inform Dove that you will not be home until tonight.'

'Tyrant,' muttered Chrys, as she dialled London and the number of the office where her sister would be at work. Anton watched her and waited long enough for her to be in speaking contact with Dove, then he sauntered in the direction of the kitchen and left her to explain that she was down in Kent still and would be staying the day as the weather was so good.

'Are you alone with *him*?' Dove's voice echoed along the line with a thrill of curiosity and indignation in it.

'Are you being quite wise, Chrys? I mean, you know what he is! His reputation is awful where women are concerned!'

'It isn't quite true.' Chrys was surprised by the cool authority of her assertion. 'I don't know how it ever got about that he's women-mad—actually he isn't a Casanova at all but much more of a lone wolf.'

'Still a wolf, darling, so mind he doesn't eat you up.' Dove gave a laugh. 'Do you like him, Chrys? Come on, open up to your sister at least. Do you find him good-looking?'

Chrys thought of the lean, wicked distinction of his face, in which were set those mercurial grey eyes, slanting outwardly, and densely lashed 'Yes,' she said briefly. 'The fact of the matter is that I'm here as the guest of his grandmother, so for heaven's sake, don't go jumping to any romantic conclusions, Dove. She's a wonderful woman and has danced in ballet herself, so we have plenty to talk about.' Chrys knew she was fibbing a bit, but she really didn't want Dove to get the idea that a romance was about to bloom between herself and a man who was merely using her as a distraction. A man who had been wooed by titled women didn't fall in love with a girl such as herself.

'Oh, so he has a family here in England?' said Dove, surprised and just a little note of disappointment in her voice, as if she had half-hoped that Chrys was in danger of a romantic seduction. She had often asserted that Chrys was too cool about men and needed to have her heart shaken up. 'I didn't know about that.'

'Well, you know now, sister dear, and you can return to your typewriter and your thoughts of Jeremy without being anxious about me and my honour.' Even

as Chrys used the word she rather wondered if it would
still be intact at the end of the day. Was she quite
certain that she could handle a man like Anton? Her
nerves quivered, forcibly, as he suddenly appeared in
the alcove from the interior of the flat and stood there
silently, framed by the arch in his dark narrow pants
and his soft white shirt, his eyes narrowed like a
pleasured cat.

'Bye, Dove! Yes, I shall be sure to make the most of
the sunshine.' The receiver sang as Chrys laid it in the
cradle, and thrusting her hands into the pockets of
the hip-length jacket she stood there daring those grey
eyes that glinted behind the double lashes that were
black as soot. Her heart beat quickly—had he caught
the word she had used a moment ago? She hoped to
goodness he had not. It might give him ideas! If he
needed any?

'The food basket will be ready in a while,' he said
blandly. 'We can buy you a swimsuit at the beach, and
possibly some suntan oil. Your skin is very fair and
must be protected. How easy, Chrysdova, to protect
the outer covering, but always what is inside us must
remain vulnerable, eh?'

'You don't strike me, *milor*, as being at all vulnerable,' she rejoined. 'You have remarkable assurance,
which I believe it would take a lot to shake.'

'You think I am hard and arrogant?' His expression
didn't change, but she saw the sudden flexing of his
forearm muscles, as if he controlled an urge of some
sort—perhaps to shake her, a mere slip of a girl who
dared to say honestly what she thought of him. Far too
many women had flattered him, and so made him
contemptuous of them. Did he desire to be contemptu-

ous of her? Was this his reason for making her stay the day with him? Was he out to prove that she was like all the rest—out to get a man.

She tilted her chin and the pure contours of her face revealed the pride she felt in her independence. '*Les extrêmes se touchent*,' she said in French. 'We are so extreme you and I that we are bound to clash as individuals. I think you have great charm and that you use it deliberately to play games with people. People think of you as a sort of modern-day Casanova, but you don't really love women, do you? You really like to be cruel to them in revenge——' There she broke off and colour stormed into her cheeks. What was she saying? Whatever had led her to speak like this? Was she attempting to *reform* the man?

'Don't stop there,' he drawled, 'just as you were about to tell me that I am not a great lover at all but really a great fraud.'

'Well, you are,' she flung at him. 'All the time you are secretly laughing at women for falling for you. You judge them all by your mother—except for Miroslava, and she, of course, is an exceptional person. Such people are rare.'

'Are they, Chrysdova?' His direct stare was very disconcerting. 'So rare, do you think, that I am never likely to find one for my own?'

'Not if you go on looking in all the wrong places,' she rejoined. 'I think in your heart that you distrust love and so you avoid it by meeting people you know you don't really like. Sophisticated people——'

'Like my mother, eh?'

'I imagine she was like that.'

'Lovely and heartless—the mirage and never the real oasis.'

'Yes—but it really isn't any of my business.' Suddenly she was in desperate retreat from the subject and wished she had never mentioned it. She cast him a quick, almost appealing look, and then hastened in the direction of the *salon*. Miroslava was there to offer a little protection from him for a little while longer.

An hour later Chrys was inevitably alone with Anton for the rest of the day, beside him in his car as they drove through the sunlight in search of the sea and the sandy beach at Applegate.

The warm breeze blew her hair from her brow and played caressingly about her neck. She had to relax from this maddening tension which had built up between herself and Anton, and closing her eyes she willed the relaxation of the ballet dancer just before the curtain rose out there on stage. She coaxed each toe, each finger, each separate muscle to uncoil, and she told herself that the best way to get through this day with Anton was to pretend to herself that it was a piece of theatre and not to be taken seriously for one moment. She must enjoy it as she would a *pas de deux* with a particularly expert dancer, and not allow anything he said or did to impose itself on her inner self. She knew him for what he was. She knew that he came to Europe in search of fun and that his real life lay in the desert.

The old dancing discipline imposed on herself she allowed her eyes to open and met the sun with a smile. 'It is an enchanting day,' she said. 'It really would have been wasted in stuffy London.'

'I understood that it had become swinging London,'

he murmured. 'I must say that on this occasion I have noticed some oddly dressed, and rather shaggy young people around the town. They all seem to have diddy bags with them and to look in a perpetual trance, as if they never stop walking.'

'I believe a lot of them are tourists from other countries,' said Chrys, and her smile deepened. 'Tourists of a slightly different calibre from yourself, *milor*. One could never say that you are oddly dressed and ungroomed, and I am sure your worldly possessions would not fit into a diddy bag, as you call it.'

'I have fitted them into a desert tent before now,' he rejoined. 'We have our herds at El Kadir and I have more than once followed them into the hills with the men.'

'What is it like,' she asked, 'to be the lineal head of a desert tribe? I gather that you are.'

'I am. My father was accepted as almost a son by the Sheik who befriended Miroslava, and when he died a hero fighting off a raid it was decided by the various clansmen that I take his place. The Sheik's workers and servants had been in his family for generations; born and bred to his leadership, and his own sons died as boys. His workers loved my father, and it seemed natural enough that I take his place. The people bring their debts and sins and troubles to me, and I sit in judgment on them. This may sound arrogant to you, but it is a natural way of life in the desert. I take responsibility, and when I am absent the job falls to my deputy who has the impressive name of Haroun bin Raid.'

'Tell me about Belle Tigresse.' She had relaxed almost unaware, for in the strangest way he seemed much nicer when he took on, in a manner of speaking, his desert cloak.

'It is a large, white-walled house with a central dome, set within a walled garden that shelters it from the desert winds and the summer *khamsin*. It has shutters of blue, and the doors are painted blue—to ward off the evil eye.' Anton gave her a quick side-glance. 'Did you know that blue is the colour the Devil cannot tolerate? That he hides from it as if it might blind him? It is the colour of heaven, sky and sea. The colour of the Madonna's cloak. And the colour of the Son of God's eyes. Did you know, *mutushka*?'

She shook her head, and tried not to believe that his words had also shaken her heart.

'What are the social events in the desert?' she asked quickly.

'Births and marriages are our main events.' Now a thread of amusement ran through his voice. 'These are much celebrated, and my *chef* makes a huge *cou-cous d'honneur* to send to the family in which a marriage or a birth has taken place. The head of the family sends to me in return, as Sidi of the tribe, a huge slice of wedding cake, or a box of sugared almonds from the baptism of the child. This is called *baraka*, the good will between man and master.'

'Don't you attend their parties?' she asked, for a sudden picture of him all alone in his white-walled house arose in her mind, stretched on a divan, grey eyes half-closed against the smoke of a narrow strong cheroot.

'Occasionally. Arab weddings are odd, erotic affairs, but sometimes in the evening of a christening there will be a fire dance, which is to say that bonfires are lit and couples dance around them, and the old half-Spanish, half-Moorish songs are sung, for most of the musicians that attend these festivities are from the cities such as Fez and Morocco. They are marvellously evocative songs. You should hear them, *matushka*. You would enjoy them.'

'I am sure I would.' And now in place of that lonely figure she had imagined, she saw him cloaked by fire-light, a slumbrous delight agleam in his eyes as he listened to the barbaric music of the East.

'Why do you come to Europe when your heart is in the desert?' she asked him.

'To see Miroslava, my child. And to singe my wings in the way of a bachelor. I am thirty-three, Chrysdova. Would you have me live like a monk?'

'It is none of my business how you live, Prince Anton.' She had expected him to be honest, but all the same she didn't like the little sting his honesty left like a welt across her own guarded heart and body.

'Would you sooner hear that I keep a *harem* at *Belle Tigresse*?' he mocked. 'I leave alone the daughters of my desert clansmen, not because I don't find them lovely, but because I should soon have a *harem* on my hands if I dared make love to any of those girls. Their fathers would then make me a gift of them—do you see how it is?'

Suddenly she did see and her sense of humour re-asserted itself. 'Yes, I do see, *milor*. Better to make a fool of a society belle, even if it means getting shot for your trouble.'

He laughed softly by her side, with a sort of purring menace. 'I was not having an affair with that particular young lady, but no matter. You must understand that I am several men in one. I have Russian blood in which there is also Tartar blood. I was born in a desert house, the son of a Russian and a Frenchwoman from Paris. I was brought up among tribesmen, sent to France to be educated, and to serve for a while in her army. I sometimes wonder myself if my soul has the shape of a triangle.'

This time Chrys laughed. 'Do you feel strange when you come to Kent, *milor*? It is all so very English, so green with a vista of blue where the sea locks in the land.'

'English as yourself, *matushka*. Gold, blue and green.' The meaning in his voice was all too plain, and a quick glance at his profile showed her the line of silent laughter beside his mouth. He swung the car with graceful expertise around a bend in the road and there ahead of them lay one of those arrestingly pretty villages only to be seen in England, with cottage-type houses in which hollyhocks stood tall and deep-belled in the small front gardens, and with a small inn about halfway down the road, its black and white timbering catching the sunlight and its mullioned windows like gleaming, friendly eyes.

'Would you like to stop for a drink?' Anton asked her. 'We have plenty of time—all day, in fact, to spend at the beach.'

'It would be nice,' she said. 'It does look a quaint old place—and so very English.'

He laughed in that purring way of his and turned the car into the driveway fronting the inn, which was named the Plough. The car slid to a smooth halt and Anton leaned over to open the door beside Chrys, and at once she was on the defensive against his physical

112

closeness, and the brush of his darkly lashed eyes over her face.

'Are you to be your sister's bridesmaid?' he asked, unexpectedly.

'Why—yes.' She was startled by his question, and this widened her eyes and intensified their blueness as she looked at him, held there in her seat by his extended arm.

'Have you no wish yourself, *matushka*, to be a bride?'

'I told you—marriage would interfere with my career.'

'Marriage would become you,' he murmured. 'You were made for a man, not for an audience to enjoy.'

'Anton—please——'

'Please?' He quirked an eyebrow and leaned a little nearer to her, so that she felt the warmth of his brown skin and felt in him all the vital desires of a man in the very prime of life. 'What would you like me to do to please you—treat you as if you were my maiden aunt?'

'Be nice and don't flirt,' she pleaded. 'Tomorrow we both go our separate ways and this—this could be a day to remember without regret.'

'Would you regret my lovemaking?' His tone was half-mocking, and yet his eyes were beautifully still and serious. 'I should light a candle in a chapel to the memory of it. Beauty and innocence are a rare conquest, these days.' So saying he flung open the car door, and she caught the brief ravishment of his eyes as she fled from him into the inn. It was cool in there, with a few people seated on the oak settles, or leaning against the bar. Heads turned to study her, and then the man who followed her into the lounge. The way these Kent farmers looked at Anton made her want to laugh, nervously. He was so very foreign by contrast to them. So tall and dark and illimitably sure of himself. His fingers sought her elbow and she knew instinctively that he was letting the other men know that she was his!

She didn't pull away ... it was safe to surrender to him ... in the company of other people.

'And what will you have, sir?' As always Anton commanded service without raising an eyebrow. He glanced at Chrys and she said she would have a Campari and soda.

'Make that two,' he said to the barman, after which he took a long, interested look round the lounge, while Chrys seated herself on one of the bar stools and tried to look as composed as the various glances in their direction would allow.

'I believe,' Anton murmured, 'these good people think we are a couple of the jet set. Do you mind? That I have this odd effect on the English?'

She smiled a little and knew that his question held a double meaning.

'You have the look of what you are, *milor*,' she said.

'And what is that, *matushka*?' He gazed down at her with mocking eyes.

'Prince Lucifer!'

'You dare to say that—here. Would you care to say it when we are alone?'

'Why, don't you care for the truth?' She gave a laugh and lifted her drink to her lips. 'You are fond of dishing it out to other people, I have noticed.'

'So I am! So you think of me as the dark angel, eh? Fallen from the good graces of heaven?'

114

'Mmmm.' She nodded. 'Ever since we met you have been trying to make me fall—now haven't you, Prince —Anton?'

His eyes held hers, glinting like steel, mesmeric, shutting out all other faces so that only his dark face filled her world in that moment. 'From the first moment we entered that lift, you and I, we were like two stars bound upon a clash. The impact has been shattering, eh? When we part neither of us will easily forget this meeting—confess that, at least!'

'Of course I confess it,' she said. 'It isn't every day that a girl meets Lucifer in the flesh.'

His eyes slowly narrowed in a smile ... a dangerous smile. 'If you want me to prove that I am no angel, *chérie*, then you are going the right way about it.' His fingers touched her bare arm for the briefest moment, and it was as if a flame ran over her. She tautened ... for there was in his touch a bewitching, enslaving, seducing quality.

'I am a person, not a puppet,' she retorted. 'You can't do just as you please with me. I have more to do with my life than be *your* plaything for the little while it takes you to become bored with your toys.'

'Do you really believe that my life is littered with discarded playthings?' He laughed a little and drank his Campari. 'Is it part of your defence that you have to believe me entirely cruel? Dare you not believe that I can also be tender?'

'*L'amour tendre,*' she murmured. 'And then *l'amour tragique.*'

'My child, I avoid hearts that I might break,' he drawled. 'Tell me, am I in danger of breaking yours?'

'Mine, *milor*, is given to my career.'

115

'Then if I make love to you I cannot really harm you—not if your heart is not involved.'

'My pride would be involved, *milor*, and I don't care to be the caprice of a Russian prince, thank you all the same for the offer.'

'If I had to in the desert, you piece of English ice, I would soon have you melting. You have no idea how seducing the desert can be upon the senses, especially at night when all is silent and the stars flood the sky and the jasmine awakes in the enclosed gardens. I see you there, in a lovely silk robe of blue, the border of each hanging sleeve embroidered with *fleurs de lys*.' He lit a cheroot as he spoke and flame and smoke tangled together in the glance he gave her. 'There is a place to which I ride when the dawn arises all veined with black and scarlet. I call it the Jade Oasis, and never on this earth was there a place more lovely, or more lonely. Think of riding with me, *dorogaya*. Does your blood not stir in your veins, Chrysdova?'

It did ... uncomfortably so, and she didn't protest when he indicated to the barman that two more drinks be brought to them. She wanted her senses to be dulled, not tingling as he had just set them tingling with his too vivid description of his wonderful oasis.

'Have you taken many of your European conquests to see your Jade Oasis?' she asked in a deliberately cool voice. 'I am sure they were enchanted, by the place and by your escort.'

'Don't, child,' he leaned close to her, and his teeth gleamed white through the smoke of his cheroot, 'try me too close to the edge of my Russian temper.'

'Why—would you whip me?' She dared his eyes, her own eyes flashing jewel-blue with her defiance of

116

him and her response to what lay in the heart of his desert. Surely only a mirage and nothing that could be firmly grasped as a real and lasting heaven. She would not be coaxed by his mirage only to find herself left thirsting in the desert. He was too attractive, too devilish to be listened to.

'A whipping you could take.' His eyes raked over her, taking in the youthful pride and defiance. 'I should have to use a thousand kisses to defeat you and bend you to the sand.'

'You think I'd let you?' She gave a scornful little laugh, but avoided looking at his lips, in which a touch of cruelty mingled with a certain quirk of tenderness.

'Most women would think it cruel not to be desired,' he drawled. 'You really are an extraordinary creature, Chrysdova.'

'Why, because I resist your wiles, Prince Anton?'

'Are you quite certain they are wiles?'

'The art to charm and the ability to conquer lie in your eyes, *milor*. You are like a falcon, but I am no dove. I have been trained to obey my *maître de ballet*, but beyond that I am my own mistress and I intend to remain so.'

'You prefer water when I can give you wine?'

'What—*vin du mal*?' she shot back at him.

'That, Chrysdova, is not nice.' Instantly his fingers were about her wrist and he was making her aware of the steel and fire in his touch. 'You are a delight to the eyes, but you have a shocking distrust of men. Truly a sand cat, far readier to scratch than to purr. By heaven, I'll make you purr before I am finished with you!'

Still holding her by the wrist he pulled her from the

117

bar stool and walked her out of the inn. She didn't dare to struggle for her freedom, not in front of those people in the lounge, but when they reached the car she dug her fingernails into him and demanded her release. 'I'm not coming with you to the beach,' she flared. 'I'm going back to London.'

'Scared?' he taunted. 'Afraid of a mere man?'

'Damn brute!' she flung at him, and then gave a gasp as he swept her up in his arms and dropped her neatly into the front seat of the Rapier.

'And stay there!' he ordered, striding round to the other side and sliding in behind the wheel. 'You stay where you are, my girl, and like it!'

'I hate you!' she stormed, nursing her wrist. 'I really do hate your arrogance. It's written all over you! You're so used to playing lord of the land that you can't bear it when a mere woman stands up to you. You like women to be horizontal—weak and willing——'

'Stop it!' he ordered. 'In a moment you will be in tears.'

'Never! I wouldn't cry for you if you were——' Sharply she broke off and turned her head away from him. The car shot away from the inn and sped along the road to the sea. Tears were blinding her eyes and making a haze of the sun, and she hated that as well. Never in her life had she felt so on edge with anyone; never had life felt so complicated, not even when she had lain in a hospital bed and feared for her future as a dancer. There had been doctors to reassure her, nurses to soothe away her fears—but right now there was no one but herself to fight her battle. She was all

118

alone with Anton ... and a broken heart was harder to mend than a broken bone or two.

The beach at Applegate was long and undulating, with fine tan-coloured sands and groups of rocks at the sea's edge to make it picturesque. The waves came in to the beach in long silky swirls, whipping softly back and forth against the rocks. It wasn't a crowded beach, but Chrys was very relieved to see a few family groups, and young people in the water, their laughter flung and caught in the net of the sun and the spindrift.

After parking the car Anton had made Chrys go with him to a shop that sold beach wear, and he had bought her a white suit, a pair of scarlet waders, and a beach ball. With mockery incarnate in his eyes he had tossed the ball into her arms. 'Something for you to play with,' he had jibed. 'Something nice and safe, and if you lose it what will it matter? No one will weep over a lost beach ball, will they, *matushka*.'

Down on the beach he had sought out the attendant and hired a beach hut, and now Chrys was inside, the flap closed against intrusion while she took off her clothes and stepped into the one-piece bathing suit. As she pulled the soft white material up over her limbs, up over her hips and her bust and slipped the straps over her shoulders, she felt tiny nerves contracting in her stomach.

With an assumption of nonchalance she was far from feeling Chrys left the beach hut and was glad to find that Anton had quitted the steps and was halfway down the beach talking to a small girl. Chrys heard him laugh, and for the first time that sensuous purring sound was absent from his laughter and she felt a strange little shock of—of envy. How nice to be young enough to be unafraid of his charm ... and Chrys ran towards the sea, flying into its embrace as if in search of protection.

She was swimming lazily when Anton joined her, and she told herself he was like a lean, brown tiger-shark swimming around her, brushing her legs with his fingertips, teasing and agile, and then suddenly gone from her side as he swam out and out into the dazzle of the hot sun on the water. She told herself she wouldn't follow him, and then she just had to, for the lure of the sea was upon her and she was a good swimmer, having been born on the sea coast and possessed of parents who believed in the health giving properties of the ocean.

'Race you to the beach!' he called out, when she had almost caught up with him.

She turned with all the grace of her dancing body and side by side they swam back to the sands, into the waves that were curling there. Anton gave a hand to her and almost unthinking she took it and was drawn to him as if she were a pin, a feather, a plume of bright water, her hair a long wet mane unloosened from its knot, and each curve of her slender body almost nude in the thin white covering of the bathing suit.

She had no time to catch her breath as a warm wet arm locked itself about her, firm as whipcord, and not to be denied. His mouth came down to hers and with a kind of sea-drugged, sun-drugged compliance she allowed her lips to be taken and roughly, firmly caressed by his. Her hands came up against his chest, half protesting, and then stilled by the shock of pleasure, contracting all the many tiny, sentiently placed nerves in her slim, cloistered body.

He was so close to her, all pewter smooth and firmly muscled, that it was as if for a split moment in time, a forked second of pure lightning, they were fused into a smouldering unit of one. It was he who drew away first, leaving on her mouth, and on her waist, the impress of his lips and his hands. She tossed back her hair and unable to meet his eyes she looked instead at the long, deep scar on the left side of his chest, just about where his heart would be.

'Ma doue!' His eyes were shimmering. 'What a swim —and what a kiss!'

'You'd have hurt me if I hadn't let you.' High on her cheekbones she could feel a flush, and on her lips she could still taste the sea water from his lips ... so intimate, almost like the taste of tears. 'It is easy enough for men to be brutes—they know very well that women are sensitive to pain.'

'Hush, child!' His arm swept down as if he were a Czarist cutting down a malcontent. 'Don't be so sure that men can't feel pain in the very marrow of them. They are equally human, and you have a lot to learn about them.'

'Do you plan to be my tutor?' she demanded. 'Was that lesson number one? Good heavens, lesson number two must really be something!'

'Indeed it is.' His eyes narrowed to a shimmery grey. 'Would you like me to demonstrate? We could go straight through the course.'

He took a deliberate step towards her and she retreated so hastily that she tripped over a rock and fell to the sands before she could save herself. She lay there breathless while he towered over her and looked down at her with the threat of more of that devastating lovemaking in his gaze. She had to find a weapon against him and she began to laugh. 'Oh, Apollo, who caught at love and filled his arms with bays!'

'Chrysdova, lovely and man-scared,' he mocked. 'With hair such as yours, and that mouth, you should be all passion. On your feet, you little coward, and come give me my lunch.'

She knelt and made him a mock salaam. 'I live but to obey your commands, O lord of light. What will you have—caviare and wine?'

His hands reached for her and swung her to her feet. He bent his head and his teeth brushed her shoulder before she could pull away. 'The goose pâté was very good,' he jibed. 'Just a little salty, but nonetheless tasty.'

'You are ridiculous!' Chrys broke free of him and ran in the direction of the beach hut, and all the time she could feel that teasing, nibbling pressure of his teeth against her shoulder. She knew the name for it, she knew that it was called love play, and she told herself she would have to find some excuse to get away from this beach before the sun waned and the sea and the sands began to go dark.

She laid the checked cloth on the sands and took from the lunch basket the savouries and delectable-looking sandwiches Vera had packed for them. There was also a bottle of wine, and carefully wrapped wine glasses, and as she set these out Anton came and sprawled on the sands. 'Hand me the corkscrew,' he said. 'I know there is one because I put it in myself.'

Chrys found it and gave it to him and he proceeded

to uncork the wine. 'Make yourself comfortable,' he said, 'and don't flit about like a hostess listening for the doorbell. All who are coming to the party are present and correct.'

She sat down at the other side of their spread, opened a napkin and took a couple of sandwiches. A glass of wine was held towards her and she took it with a murmur of thanks and was relieved that her hand didn't shake. 'How chic,' she said, 'to be drinking wine at a picnic.'

'I have the feeling that you would prefer lemon squash,' he drawled. 'Much less likely to go to the head. I drink to your pure blue eyes, *matushka*, and the way they remind me of the desert sky when the blue hour approaches. Do you drink to me?'

'Why not?' She raised her glass. 'Here's to knowing you, Anton. When I dance in a Russian ballet I shall think of you.'

'I am glad to hear that you don't intend to quite forget me.' He popped a savoury into his mouth and looked at her over the rim of his wine glass. 'What ballet had you in mind—The Snow Princess?'

She smiled and nibbled a pickle. 'Do you go back soon to your desert house, *milor*? It must be a wrench for you to leave Miroslava?'

'It is,' he agreed, 'but I can no longer expect a woman of her years to endure the heat and often the loneliness. She is better at the castle. She has her music and her memories, and kind old Vera.'

'You must at times feel lonely yourself, *milor*.' Chrys took a quick sip of her wine. 'Now that your grandmother is no longer at Belle Tigresse.'

'Do you care—really—that I might now and then be

123

lonely in my desert house?' There was a little crack as he broke a hard-boiled egg and peeled the shell.

'I think when you are a little *triste* you saddle up and ride to your Jade Oasis,' she said, handing him the salt for his egg.

'Taking with me my *belle amie* of the moment?' He shook salt on to his egg and bit it in half with a snap of his teeth.

'We were talking of loneliness——'

'Ah, so we were, little one, but it is not always a fact that a man is no longer lonely because he has with him a woman—not that I have ever taken a woman to the oasis. There are two sorts of loneliness, that of the body, and that of the soul. We are locked within the prison of ourselves—perhaps only one person alone can enter with the key to our inner mystery and all our secret agonising. Perhaps only then does the rest-lessness go away like an ache that has troubled one for a long time. You must, Chrysdova, feel lonely yourself at times—and don't bother to deny it. Don't say again that your career suffices. Your trouble is that you don't trust a man to give you the same joy, the same heady sweetness that your dancing gives you. You trust in your dancing to fill your life—but what if it doesn't? What then will you have, if you let your feelings lie like frozen crocuses under that snow-cool skin of yours?'

'It is my business what I do with my life,' she rejoined. 'I don't plan to have affairs just to compensate for this year when I must remain inactive as a dancer——'

'I was not talking about affairs,' he cut in. 'You were not made for those, but you were made lovely,

124

and love will come to you whether you will it or not. If you give it the frozen shoulder, *ma petite*, it may never come again with such passion and power.'

'What would you know about love, Prince Anton?' She gave him a cool look, and yet could feel her fingers gripping the hot fine sand with nervous tension. 'To you it is just another game of roulette. Tonight the girl in red, or the one in black, and when the game grows tedious you walk away and you don't even glance back to see if the girl is weeping. If I ever loved it wouldn't be your kind of love!'

'If snow ever burns and flame ever freezes,' he mocked, and he reached for the wine bottle and there was a reckless look on his face as he filled his glass. 'Will you join me in another glass of this provocative wine that loosens the tongue?'

'No thanks,' she said, and in that instant she made up her mind to go home. She ate her sweet, an iced *purée* of fruit, and she listened to the tide coming in, and the gradual quietening of other voices on the beach. She was aware, almost without looking, when Anton turned his face against his arm and closed his eyes. She waited, patiently and quietly, and then when she dared fully to look at him, she saw his dark lashes still on his cheeks, and she saw his chest rising and falling evenly in sleep. She stared for a moment at the scar that was a crescent of white against the tan of his skin. A strange little shudder ran all through her, and then she slipped to her feet and walked silently to the beach hut. Within ten minutes she was dressed and her hair was combed. She checked her purse to make sure she had money enough for the train fare to London

... and she walked away from Anton de Casenove without looking back.

This time she would be the one to walk away ... before he did so, and left her in tears.

CHAPTER SEVEN

'WILT thou have this woman to thy wedded wife? ... Wilt thou love her, comfort her, honour and keep her ...'

At that point in her dreaming, while Dove still seemed to stand beside her bridegroom in pale satin and lace, Chrys awoke to find herself in a cabin aboard a ship, the bedclothes half off her restless figure, while deep in the heart of the vessel the engines beat firmly and regularly.

She sat up and stared at the luminous dial of her travelling clock. It was still early morning, though a faint light was outlining the window facing her bed. She could hear the soft breathing of her cabin companion in the twin bed, and she gave a slight smile. Maud Christie was well travelled and she slept soundly, undisturbed by the motion of the ship, by the strange scents that stole into the cabin, a mixture of ozone and weathered timber and a faint whiff of coffee always on the air.

Chrys, as a dancer, had travelled to various cities by jet plane, but this was the first time she had voyaged in a cargo ship that also carried a few passengers. It was a new, exhilarating experience, and today they would arrive at Port Said, and she would have her first glimpse of a desert city, on the edge of the vast and golden sea of sands.

She took a biscuit from the tin on her bedside table and made herself comfortable against her pillows as she nibbled it. Maud Christie had been doubtful about employing her at first. She had said bluntly that she had in mind a middle-aged woman used to the job of being a companion. A young, pretty toe-dancer who would attract the men like bees to a jampot was not her idea at all of what she required. They'd get halfway to their destination and some young man would steal her away and leave Maud stranded again.

'No, you're hopeless,' she had said, waving Chrys to the door. 'Go and get yourself a modelling job, young woman. It will pay better than I can, and no doubt amuse you far more.'

'It would bore me to distraction,' Chrys had laughed, for right away she had taken to Maud, with her forthright air, her solid figure in a tweed suit, and her hair that was cut short but still retained some of the gold of her youth. She had a humorous mouth, and rather fine eyes, and Chrys felt certain that she would be interesting to work for, and not too bossy.

'I thought the youth of today wanted only to enjoy the glamorous side of life, with no respect for the past, and little interest in anything but the thrill of the moment. Are you telling me, young woman, that you're different from the other members of your generation?'

'We aren't all flighty,' said Chrys. 'Some of us have a serious side, Mrs Christie.'

'Maud, if you don't mind?' The decision was as rapid as that. 'If you are going to travel to the desert

127

with me, where the sun will darken that fine white skin of yours, and where the *khamsin* can spring to life within the flickering of an eyelid.' Maud had jangled the blue Arabian beads that she wore with her English tweeds. 'There are many discomforts in the East, to match its many delights, and there will be hell to pay, I promise you, if you let me down and prove inept, or as hungry for a man as my last fool of a companion.'

'Men are my least concern.' And Chrys spoke with such decision, and even a hint of scorn, that Maud studied her somewhat critically.

'Been hurt, or let down by one of them?' she asked.

Chrys shook her head and explained that her career came first.

'A bit dangerous, that.' Maud pursed her lips. 'Love is like the *khamsin*, say the Arabs, always waiting to overwhelm the unwary.'

'I'm not unwary,' said Chrys. 'On the contrary, I'm very wary.'

'Well, let us hope so.' And after that Maud proceeded to tell Chrys what she would need for the journey, and here she was, with the sea voyage almost over and England left far behind, with its constant reminders that Dove was partly lost to her in the loving arms of Jeremy, that her parents were content with each other and their garden at Westcliff, and another member of the ballet company had stepped into her shoes and would dance the roles which had been planned for her during the forthcoming season.

This trip out East was her only consolation and Chrys was determined to make the most of it.

She was up, bathed and dressed in crisp tailored blue by the time Maud Christie joined her for breakfast at the Captain's table. The sea was looking gloriously

blue and unruffled, and Captain Laurent gallantly re-
marked that the sea was trying to compete with the
colour of Mademoiselle's eyes.

Chrys smiled at the compliment, but absently, for in
the distance she glimpsed like a mirage the gleaming
minarets and domes of an oriental city, floating on the
horizon, and making her heart beat so much faster
than the admiration of any man.

'Is it real, or am I imagining it?' She pointed towards the scene, etched so clearly by the brilliant sunlight.

'One's distant glimpse of the tropics never fails to
stimulate the imagination,' said the Captain, and his
smile was worldly and indulgent of her excitement as
his Gallic eyes dwelt on her face. 'I hope you will not
be disappointed when you actually breathe its many
aromas, mademoiselle, and discover that the sun's
gauzy veil hides an ancient and sometimes raddled
face.'

'Don't disillusion the child before she has had a
chance to see Port Said for herself,' Maud chided him.
'We seasoned travellers grow into cynics, but Chrys is
new to the world of Eastern sunlight and mysticism.
Don't listen to him, child. Frenchmen are realists
about everything, including romance. They only give
their hearts to a fine wine and well cooked food.'

'How dare you libel the world's best lovers!' Captain Laurent looked mock-injured. 'All during this all
too short voyage I had hoped that I was winning the
heart of this golden English flower, who this morning
looks as if the waves just gave birth to her, so fresh and
new and untouched by life. You are a lucky woman,
Madame Christie, to have such a companion for your
travels.'

'I am hoping I stay lucky,' Maud retorted, wiping the marmalade from her lips. 'I don't want any of you men snatching her away from me. I am a garrulous woman and I like someone to talk to in my own tongue while I pursue my own particular devil, which is the travel bug. It seems to have its roots in my feet and I can't stay in one place for long.'

A few hours later Maud's feet, and that of her companion, were on shore and their baggage was being passed through the Customs office. Maud had brought cameras and a typewriter, not to mention a casket of Indian tea, a couple of well-upholstered sleeping bags, a pressure cooker and a folding bath. These were all packed in a trunk, which had to be opened for the officer's inspection, and Maud muttered to Chrys that anyone would think she was smuggling arms into the country, the fuss they were making.

'The *sitt* plans to camp in the desert?' exclaimed the official, in passable English. 'Will that not be inconvenient for two ladies?'

'It would be,' Maud rejoined, 'if we didn't have the things you are looking over as if they're machineguns!'

The olive-faced official, in his impeccable white uniform, shook his head in the age-old puzzlement of the male Eastern intellect in conflict with the mind of the European female. He relocked the trunk and chalk marked it. 'Welcome to our country, to you and your daughter,' he said to Maud. 'May you enjoy your visit.'

'Thank you, young man.' She marched on airily out of the customs office, looking oddly pleased in that way of childless women that Chrys should be taken for her daughter. Porters followed them, carrying the baggage, and quite soon a horse-drawn arabeah was at the kerb and they climbed into it. It was shaded from the hot sun, and Chrys was delighted that Maud hadn't chosen one of the more modern closed-in cabs. Chrys settled herself for the drive to the railway station, the shadows of the awning fringe dancing against her face as Maud settled up with the men who had now loaded their cases and the much-travelled trunk on to the floor of the cab.

Then they were off, clattering gaily through the narrow streets of closely built houses, their wooden balconies forming a sort of broken bridge above the heads of the people and the various vehicles that honked and clanked their way over the uneven paving stones of the roads that ran like a maze through the town.

Chrys breathed the tangy aromas that came from the hooded shops and houses, and gazed with brilliantly alive eyes at the Eastern scene. It was still the middle of the morning, so the town was clamorous. But later on, when the sun reached its zenith, the people would disappear behind closed shutters and silence would fall over Port Said. Every shadow would stand still in the blazing heat, and not a lizard or the tail of a cat would be seen.

The strangest sight of all was outside the railway station, where a band of dancers in robes and turbans were whirling to the wailing music of pipes and drums. Chrys, who was interested in all forms of dancing, was naturally intrigued and could have stayed watching for quite a while, but Maud said they would lose their train and there wouldn't be another to Beni Kezar for hours and she wanted to reach the desert town before nightfall.

'There's a small hotel there and no real need to book

in advance for the one or two nights we shall be staying, but if we arrive late the chances are that we shan't find a porter to manage our baggage.' Maud smiled and patted Chrys on the arm. 'There will be plenty of colourful characters where we shall be going, and plenty of time for you to watch their antics.'

'Coming,' said Chrys, with a farewell glance at the dancers, and beyond them to the mosque with its great studded doors and a square shaped minaret slotted with glass like a great lantern. She saw a grey Citroen car sweep into the kerb and a heavily robed figure emerged from it, sweeping past the orange-sellers and the peddlers of charms, matches and postcards with an imperious disregard for the charms that his full sleeve swept from the tray of one of the youths.

Instinctively Chrys darted forward to help the youth retrieve his wares, and she felt the fierce glance that stabbed at her from beneath the Arabian headcloth bound with an *agal* of golden thread. She ignored the look, knowing full well that upper class Arabs disapproved of women such as herself, who saw no harm in helping the boy to pick up the cheap little charms out of the dust. Arrogant brute!

'Here you are,' she said to the boy. 'That seems to be the lot.'

He didn't understand her, of course, but with a quick shy smile he thrust one of the charms into her hand and obviously said in Arabic that she was to have it for helping him.

'Take it,' said Maud at her elbow. 'And for heaven's sake don't offer to pay for it. These people are as proud as Lucifer, and grateful as saints for a kindly helping hand. Just say to him, *naharic saide.*'

Chrys obeyed with a smile, and tucked the charm into the pocket of her blazer.

'What do the words mean?' she asked Maud, as they entered the station, with a pair of porters in tow with their belongings.

'May your day be blessed. Lovely words, aren't they? The Arabic mode of speech really is a graceful one, although the men have such throaty voices that they appear to be growling instead of speaking almost biblical language. The East was always my husband's favourite place to visit. He brought me here as a bride.' Maud laughed nostalgically. 'Although at that time I thought it rather unfeeling of him to bring me to the desert on a dig when I was dreaming of a country cottage and strolling hand in hand along a flowery lane. But I soon learned to love life *en grande tente*, surrounded by miles of untamed desert. I enjoyed digging up relics of the past alongside Malcolm, and I missed him like the devil when he died. That's the trouble with love. It doesn't die with the people who engender it ... it lives on. You might be wise, young Chrys, if you can avoid love. But on the other hand ...'

The unfinished words were significant, and Chrys said prosaically, 'I should like to send off a wire to my parents if possible. Just to let them know I've arrived safely at Port Said. My mother thought I was off to the wilds when I went to Russia, and this time she believes I shall disappear into the desert and be seen no more!'

'The telegraph desk is in this direction.' Maud led the way through the clamour of the crowd, and when they reached the counter, she left Chrys to write her wire while she went to the news-stand to buy papers and magazines for the train journey. It wasn't until Chrys had her fair head bent over her task that she suddenly felt a hand feeling its way stealthily into her pocket. She knew that her face blanched as she realised that her pocket was being picked, and she swung round with a cry of protest which immediately caught the attention of a tall, robed figure at an adjoining counter. There was a flash of arrogant eyes within the shadow of the *burnous*; a glimpse of a thin dark moustache across the upper lip of the lean, foreign face. It was the same man who had knocked the charms from the peddler's tray, and Chrys wished to goodness that she had kept a tighter hold on her nerves. The pickpocket had slid away into the crowd, and all that he took with him was the cheap little charm, for obeying Maud's injunction Chrys carried her purse firmly in her hand.

'*Pardon, mademoiselle!*' The Arab spoke in accented French. 'You have some further trouble with a youth of the town?'

She flushed vividly, for the sarcastic words implied that she was a flirt who had been asking to be annoyed. 'It is perfectly all right, m'sieur. Someone trod on my foot.'

'I thought for a moment that you had been robbed.' He made a significant movement with a lean, sun-dark hand. 'Women such as yourself are a natural target for the bold, bad element swarming here in Port Said.'

'What do you mean—women like myself?' Her eyes blazed in her face, from which the flush had abruptly fled leaving her cheeks pale with annoyance. It seemed to her that the arrogant superiority of this Sheik, as she supposed he was, was far more infuriating than the

134

sidling up to her of a petty thief. The thief had got away with something valueless, but this man seemed to imply that she was a fool ... or worse.

'You are a tourist, are you not?' he said. 'On your first trip to the East, I presume. You should be more on your guard, *mademoiselle*. The next time an attempt might be made to steal your person.'

'Really!'

'Yes, really.' The eyes that glinted within the folds of the gold-roped headcloth seemed to be infinitely mocking, and yet at the same time diabolically in earnest. Then as Maud approached the counter, the Arab bowed and strolled off with a tall, haughty self-assurance, making no sound as he moved away, like an alert and graceful animal.

'Don't tell me you've been flirting with one of the local Sheiks?' said Maud, half amused, and half serious. 'It doesn't do——'

'On the contrary! The darned man was being officious and sarcastic.' Chrys gazed after him with fury in her eyes, noticing how the crowd fell back to give passage to his robed figure. 'He seemed to imply that I should be on a lead and not allowed to run free. I expect he's one of those who has a harem filled with tame gazelles!'

'Very likely,' laughed Maud. 'Now have you sent off your wire?'

'No, but I won't be a moment.' Chrys quickly scribbled a message of reassurance to her parents and handed the form to the clerk. Then she went with Maud to the train, where they settled themselves in a first-class carriage, and Chrys listened to the excited voices of the passengers and the porters, and remembered amidst the strangeness of it all the accident at a London railway station which had led her to this moment. Her face was reflective, and after several moments she became aware that Maud was gazing at her with a hint of curiosity.

'Still thinking about your brush with the Sheik?' she asked.

Chrys shook her head. 'He had the type of arrogance I hoped I'd seen for the last time. There was something in his manner—a sort of mocking superiority—which reminded me of someone else. I suppose men of the East, and those who assume their ways, have an affinity—but it's rather disturbing to suddenly see it again.'

'The men who inspire anger and fury, and a sort of fear, are deeply fascinating to some women.' Maud opened a magazine with an air of casualness. 'Sure you aren't fascinated?'

'Quite sure,' said Chrys, and suddenly she laughed. 'For someone who threatened me with hell if I should lose my head over a man, you seem, Maud, determined to awake my interest in one of the brutes.'

'It isn't that,' said Maud. 'I merely find it hard to believe that someone as pretty as yourself should have her head so well screwed on. Any other girl would have been in a regular dither of excitement to be spoken to by a Sheik. He was obviously that from the look of him, and the manner. You do realise that some of these personages have a lineage as ancient as that of an English duke? They expect to be treated as if the sun shines out of their eyes.'

'Especially by a member of the female sex, eh?' Chrys crossed her long slim legs and admired the blue and white styling of her court shoes. 'Well, I don't suppose we shall be seeing that particular desert hawk again, so I'm not about to worry that I spoke up to him instead of swooning.'

'I saw him board this train, as a matter of fact.' Maud flicked the pages of her magazine. 'He entered a reserved compartment, with the curtains drawn, and for all we know he might be travelling to Beni Kezar. Destiny, or *kismet* as the Arabs call it, might throw you into his path again. If so, then you'd better give him a smile or two. He may be the local *kaid*, who has the power to give or withhold permission for horses and porters to be supplied for our trip to the ruins.'

'He may be no more than an overbearing Arab with an inflated sense of his own importance,' said Chrys. 'Ah, the train is starting! We're on our way!'

'You sound like an eager kid on her way to a sandy beach instead of the vast and mysterious desert.' Maud looked indulgent. 'I'm glad you aren't the nervous sort, or haven't you yet realised that the desert is hot and lonely and unpredictable?'

Chrys thought over Maud's words, and for the first time she seemed to realise that she was heading into a world of lonely vistas and hot bright noons filled with the silence of eternity. Her blue eyes dwelt on her employer and for the briefest of moments a little fear and uncertainty stirred in their depths. She had given no heed to her parents' suggestion that she work in Westcliff and live at home with them during her year of enforced retirement from her ballet career. She had rushed headlong into this job, as if she needed desperately to get away from England, and it was only now that she felt a sense of dislocation, the jolt of being miles from the safety and security of the seaside town where she had been born and gone to school, and knew every street.

'Chrys, have I made you feel uncertain?' Maud asked.

At once the hint of fear was veiled by Chrys's lashes. She shook her head. 'The strangeness of it all just swept over me—you know, a feeling of being wafted as if on a magic carpet from the places so well known to the edge of the unknown. I read somewhere that the desert is a sphinx, which accepts some people and rejects others.'

'It is a place of moods,' Maud agreed. 'It can be capricious, and inclined like a jealous lover to expect total surrender to its mixed charms. Look out of the window, Chrys, and see the unveiling of some of those charms.'

Chrys looked and caught her breath in delight. The train swept past a huge oasis of towering palms, whose sleek trunks and pendant leaves were reflected in the mirror-like surface of a huge pool. On the edges of the oasis there was a native village, and the inhabitants could be seen going about their tasks in their dark blue robes, while camels stood tethered like sand-coloured idols among the trees.

It was like a tapestry, vividly seen and then swiftly out of focus as the train sped on its way.

It was the first glimpse Chrys had had of the pastoral East, almost a scene from the Old Testament itself, and her quick sense of adventure swiftly banished from her eyes, and her thoughts, that flash of alienation. She sat close to the window and drank in the various scenes of village life, to which Maud was so accustomed that she read a magazine article while Chrys absorbed with

138

growing wonder the sand-gardens of the village dwellers, the children with dark-honey skins, graceful and thin as fawns as they darted among the houses of sun-dried mud, flat-roofed and slotted with narrow dark windows and doors.

Cups of tea were brought to them about noon, and Maud unpacked the sandwiches and tomatoes which the *chef* of the cargo ship had supplied. 'I don't care for the lunches served on trains,' she said. 'The chops are usually tough and everything is smothered in mint sauce.'

Chrys was perfectly happy to lunch here in their compartment, picnic fashion. The sandwiches, some of smoked salmon and others of thinly sliced beef, were delicious, and she knew in her secret thoughts that she didn't fancy seeing again that tall, fierce Arab with the black moustache like a whiplash across his upper lip. He had seemed capable of carrying out any threat to a woman, being what he was, an Arab to whom women were mere objects of pleasure, or displeasure.

She ate a beef sandwich and felt certain that like the desert itself the attitudes of its men had not changed for centuries. It was not a country to engender, or invite change. It was ruled by the hands, which encroached upon each mile of cultivation like the greedy seas that gnawed the cliffs of northern lands. Already she had glimpsed one or two veiled women, and the strangeness of those covered faces still lingered in her mind to underline the *purdah* attitudes still deeply ingrained in the Eastern soul.

After lunch it grew terribly warm in the compartment, and though Maud drowsed, Chrys found the heat almost suffocating and all at once she had to escape into the corridor to try and get a breath of air.

She arose from her seat and carefully opened the door of the carriage. She stepped outside and immediately felt a welcoming breeze along the passageway. She had discarded her blazer and it was such a relief to feel the slight coolness against her neck and her bare arms.

Lost in her relief, leaning with eyes half-closed as the train sped through the hot sunlight towards its destination, she was unaware of a figure at the far end of the corridor until the aroma of a cigarette began to steal to her on that whisper of a breeze. But for several moments more her relaxation was undisturbed, until suddenly her nostrils taughtened, her senses grew alert, and every nerve in her body came alive to the fact that the aroma of the smoke was strangely familiar ... and had no place to be so, here on this oriental train!

Her eyes flashed open and she turned her head and saw instantly the tall figure in the flowing robes. He stood yards away from her, silent and still, and yet directly she noticed him he became as intrusive as a bee inside the glass of the windows.

Even as a sense of animosity flickered through her, the familiarity of the cigarette smoke was explained. She must have caught a whiff of it on his robes, when she had stood near to him at the telegraph counter. She resented his presence, even though he seemed unaware of her. He made it seem almost compulsory that she return to the guardianship of Maud, to sit sedately in that stuffy carriage until the afternoon heat waned and gave the relief that she wanted right now.

Well, she wouldn't retreat, unless he had the nerve to approach her.

He didn't stir an inch in her direction, yet all the time Chrys remained in the corridor she was aware of him, and she hated the strength of his silent personality and the unsettling effect he had upon her. In the end she wanted to return to the calm company of Maud, and when she finally did so she felt ridiculously like a female in flight.

She didn't tell Maud that she had seen the Arab again, but was glad when as the sunset flared over the sands the train arrived at Beni Kezar and they were kept too busy checking their baggage as it was loaded on to a trolley to notice if the Arab left the train at the same station as themselves.

'That seems to be eveything,' said Maud. 'Now let's get to the hotel for a cool bath, and a nice hot dinner.'

'Amen to that,' said Chrys, and as they left the station into the dusk of the evening she glanced up at the sky and saw a shooting star falling through the velvety darkness. 'Oh, look! How lovely, Maud!'

'You might think so,' said Maud drily. 'The arabs believe that a shooting star is an arrow of Allah thrown to pierce an earthly devil.'

'It could be cupid at work,' jested Chrys, and then she caught her breath as a moment before they entered their cab she saw a tall, unmistakable figure enter an adjacent cab and drive off into the night.

Maud gave her an enquiring look as she caught her small gasp. 'I hope the "arrow" hasn't pierced you, Chrys.'

Chrys smiled, and once again she kept silent about seeing the Arab, but as their cab swept through the dark streets to the hotel she prayed fervently that they wouldn't see him there, lording it over everyone.

141

It wasn't a large hotel and they were soon shown to their adjoining rooms, with a bathroom close by. 'I'm dying for a bath, so it's age before beauty,' said Maud. 'I'm told that dinner is at eight, so we have plenty of time to dress for it. See you later!'

Left entirely alone at last, Chrys unpacked what she would need for the night, and then went out on the balcony to take a look at Beni Kezar by the light of the stars. Plumbago plant sprawled all over the ironwork of the balcony, and the air held a tangy freshness which Chrys breathed in to the bottom of her lungs. That air came from the desert, she surmised, and she leaned forward and explored with her eyes the rooftops and minarets of this desert town. Beyond its walls lay the savage, untamed sands. Wild, relentless place of dreams, and demonic sunlight. Scandalous and secretive as a woman, holding, so it was said, heaven and hell for those who dared to travel there.

There were ruins about fifteen miles from Beni Kezar which Maud wanted to see again. She had last visited the place with her husband, and Chrys suspected that her employer wished to renew old memories far more than she wished to search for relics.

Anyway, whatever her reason it would be interesting, and would surely add to Chrys's own experiences of life.

She returned to her bedroom, to find Maud in the adjoining doorway, towelling her short hair. 'The bathroom is all yours, Chrys. The hot water system hums like a rocket about to take off, but it actually works. Mmm I feel so refreshed after that stuffy train journey, so now you cut along and have your soak.'

Chrys was off at a run, and there in the ornately tiled

bathroom she emptied about half a bottle of cologne into the water and sank her slim body into it with a sigh of sheer luxury. She splashed about for as long as she dared, and returned to her room feeling thoroughly refreshed herself. She was almost dressed for dinner and putting on her nylons when Maud entered, clad in beige lace and winding the small gold watch on her wrist. 'It's nice to dress up,' she said, 'and we shan't be able to in the desert. Shirts and shorts will be the order of the day there—my, Chrys, you do have nice hair! Mine was almost that colour when I was a girl, but the years and many hot suns have taken out all the colour and left me quite grey. You are almost Nordic, Chrys. Any of that blood in your family?'

'Not as far as I know. My sister Dove is fairer still.' Chrys fixed her floss-combed hair into a tortoiseshell slide, and ran a powder-puff over her face.

'When we get into the desert, Chrys, I'm going to suggest that you wear a hat. I have a floppy-brimmed one which will suit you. The Arabs rather like golden hair—it's such a contrast to the brunette hair of their own wives and girls.'

'Now don't you go telling me that I'm likely to be carried off,' Chrys protested, half laughing, and half serious. 'That darned Arab threatened me with the same fate!'

'The one at the station?' Maud stared at Chrys, the smile wiped from her lips. 'You realise that he's here at Beni Kezar?'

'So you noticed as well?'

'Could hardly avoid doing so. He's unusually tall, and those golden head-ropes mean he's an important man. Did he really make such a threat?'

143

'Well, I felt a hand in my pocket—that little charm was stolen while I was at the telegraph counter, and he noticed and said I had better be careful or someone might steal *me* next time.'

'Very likely he was kidding you,' said Maud, 'but let's hope we don't run into him again. I don't suppose he's the *kaid* of Beni Kezar, or there would have been a contingent of bodyguards with him. He's probably a local landowner, with a big house somewhere on the edge of town.'

'With high walls and a *harem* somewhere inside them.' Chrys tilted her nose in scorn. 'If he has ideas about adding me to his collection, then he's in for a shock. I was once told that I'd scratch like a sand cat if I was ever taken advantage of.'

'I believe you would, at that.' Maud looked her companion over, and a hint of worry showed in her eyes. 'You dress so simply and manage to look so eye-catching. I wonder if I did right to take you on as a companion. This place is half off the map, and some of its people are still rather primitive. Chrys, when we make camp in the desert, promise me that you'll never stray too far away. I don't know how I'd face your parents if anything happened to you.'

'Maud, I'm twenty-two and perfectly capable of taking care of myself.' Suddenly it was Chrys who was offering Maud reassurance. 'I'm sure I'm far too thin to attract the roving eye of an Arab. I thought they fed their women on honey and doughnuts in order to make them nice and plump. Look at me! I haven't an ounce of fat on me.'

'True,' said Maud, breaking into a smile. 'Let's go and remedy that right now. I'm ravenous!'

They locked their doors and made their way down to the hotel dining room. There were very few guests, and they were the only Europeans at the present time. A waiter conducted them to an alcove table, where in comparative privacy they ordered their meal from the man, who was clad in spotless white, except for a red cumerbund and turban. Maud ordered for both of them, juicy lamb cutlets, runner beans, and creamed potatoes. As a starter, savouries wrapped in vine leaves, with a plate of rice and mushrooms. She vetoed wine, murmuring in an aside to Chrys that Arabs looked down on women who imbibed. Instead she asked for Arabian coffee, which was brought to them with their savouries.

'It was a rich, hot, satisfying meal, and Chrys was able to eat with appetite because that arrogant Sheik was nowhere in sight to watch her every action. No doubt he was enjoying *kous-kous*, surrounded by his adoring flock of kohl-eyed concubines!

'You'll have a sweet to finish with?' said Maud.

'Please, but nothing too sweet after that very satisfying dinner. Fruit perhaps.'

'Fruit it shall be.' Maud called the waiter and told him they should like some grapes, washed in ice-water. While they waited for the grapes to be brought to them, Chrys fingered the bowl of apricot-coloured roses which stood on the table. For some reason they made her think of high white walls and rambling cloisters, and sheets of greenery studded with these delicate and highly scented roses.

She gave a start as another of the silent-footed waiters came to her side and with a small bow handed her a small box, waxed and sealed, but unmistakably with her name printed on the label.

'What is it? What does he say, Maud?' She looked at the package as if it contained a small bomb.

'He says a man brought it and requested that it be given to Mademoiselle Devrel. Take it, Chrys,' Maud urged, 'and stop looking as if it might explode in your face.'

'Whatever can it be?' Chrys took the box and murmured her thanks to the waiter. 'No one here knows my name, apart from the hotel manager.'

'It looks to me suspiciously like a present,' said Maud. 'Do open it and find out, or I shall bust a stitch with curiosity.'

'But I don't know anyone here at Beni Kezar who could be sending me a present. It must be a hoax!' Picking up a knife, Chrys inserted the blade under the seal and broke it. Then she lifted the lid of the box and found inside a small card, and with a frown she read the few words written upon it in perfect French .'A small token to replace what was removed from your pocket.' Without speaking Chrys handed the card to Maud, who read it and then looked at Chrys significantly.

'What has he sent you to replace the charm?'

Chrys lifted the cottonwool in the box and disclosed a tiny gold hand, perfectly made, with a blue gem set in the back of it. 'Look, Maud!'

'The Hand of Fatma, and a very beautiful example of the charm.' Maud looking intently at Chrys. 'I know you will want to refuse it, knowing who has sent it to you, but I would advise you against returning it to the Sheik. He will not only be highly insulted, but out here no one takes lightly the significance of Fatma's hand. You will see it impressed into the walls and lintels of the houses, and women hang the charm around the necks of their newborn children. It is said to bring good fortune to those who wear it.'

'But, Maud, this charm is made of gold, and the gem in the back of it looks like a small sapphire. How can I accept from such a man a gift like this? He may presume that I wish to encourage him, and that's the last thing I want to do!'

'Not if you accept the charm with a polite little note. You know, "Dear Sir, It is good of you to send me the Hand of Fatma, and I feel certain it will make my visit to Beni Kezar a pleasant one." There's nothing coy or inviting about that sort of note.'

'You seem to be making it a point of honour that I accept the charm.' Chrys fingered its smoothness, with each detail of the hand etched with minute perfection, adorned by that gleaming little sapphire. It was as if he had had her eyes in mind, and she gave a little shiver as she remembered the glint of his eyes within the almost monk-like head-covering which had prevented her from seeing his face clearly. All she knew for certain was that he wore a thin dark moustache, which was somehow significant of the inherent danger of the man.

'I believe he meant to put me in an awkward position,' she said to Maud. 'He probably thinks that I will return the charm and give him cause to feel insulted, so I'm going to surprise him and keep it. It's really rather pretty, isn't it?'

Maud smiled a little, for Chrys spoke with a touch of defiance which revealed her inmost doubts about accepting the golden hand. 'Oriental men are darned subtle,' she said, popping a black grape into her mouth. 'But I certainly think it better for you to accept the gift than refuse it. It doesn't do to offend these people, and if you type your note of thanks on my machine, then it will seem more impersonal than if you wrote it. I notice that he's highly educated. His French is far more perfect than mine. Did you notice if he was good-looking? Some of these men are extremely so, though on the other side of the coin you do find some of them as round as barrels, with enough hair on them to stuff a sofa.'

Chrys smiled absently, and wished to goodness the donor of the gift had been rotund and bearded and fatherly. She shook her head when Maud proffered the dish of grapes, and was glad when it was time to go upstairs and sleep.

She felt curiously disturbed on this her first night in the East, and it took her some time to fall asleep beneath the fine muslin swathing her bed.

On the bedside table lay the Hand of Fatma, an appealing little charm, and yet somehow significant of the subtle codes of honour and quicksilver temper of the people of the East.

CHAPTER EIGHT

DESPITE having lain awake until quite late, Chrys awoke feeling invigorated and ready for the day that lay ahead of her. She lay gazing up at the tent of pale green netting over her bed, and saw the sun as through

148

gauze striking through the long opened windows. Alien sounds drifted up from the streets that lay at either side of the hotel; she heard goat bells, and the clatter of donkey hooves, and then there came the cry of the *muezzin* from the nearby mosque. *Allah ila la Allah.* So it was still quite early, despite the warm gush of sunshine into her room.

The sun was so beckoning that Chrys could not lie idle another second and she pushed aside the yards of mosquito netting and slid out of bed. The polished wooden floor was warm under her feet, and when she glanced at her travelling clock she was surprised to find that it wasn't long after daybreak.

She opened the adjoining door and saw that Maud was still fast asleep. Well, she wasn't going to waste all this wonderful sunlight by lazing in bed herself, so Chrys hastened to the bathroom, had a wash, and returned to dress herself in narrow white trousers and a lemon shirt. She clipped back her hair, dashed lipstick over her mouth, and decided to have a look at the market stalls that were setting up in the streets below.

She felt delightfully cool, and looked it as she made her way downstairs to the foyer. There were only a couple of the staff about, emptying ashtrays and flower vases, and polishing the floor, and they gave her a rather startled look as she left the hotel. It was evident that the other guests were not such early risers, probably taking breakfast in their rooms, until it was time to go sightseeing in a horse-drawn cab.

As Chrys stepped into the street, a dozen mixed aromas sprang at her. That of Arabian coffee and spices, and the stronger smell of the goats and donkeys. She turned into an alleyway, and found herself in a

149

sort of street of coppersmiths, with highly polished bowls and pans displayed on colourful old carpets. She saw a boy glossing the surface of a great meat dish with a handful of sawdust and lemon, and heard the little hammers beating against the pewter.

Some of the traders coaxed her to buy their wares, but she walked on resolutely, knowing full well that if she stopped to admire anything she would find herself involved in a bargain for it. She turned out of the street of coppersmiths into another that sold leather goods, slippers of all colours, some of them for babies and made of the very softest of leather. There were purses and satchels for sale, and beautiful bags on a shoulder strap buckled with silver or brass. Chrys would have loved to buy one, but she hadn't enough cash with her.

She wandered through the street of silks, and came at last to the stalls selling jewellery and trinkets of every hue, some of it worthless, and some of it quite stunning. She saw a tray of charms, and was reminded of yesterday, and the Hand of Fatma which she had left on her bedside table, gleaming like a small living object as the sunlight touched it. She compared it to other similar charms she saw on the stalls, and knew that it was different, and of greater value.

She came upon carpets being sold in an open court-yard, where they were laid out to show their wonderful patterns, with several lovely Persian cats curled among them. It was like wandering into the Arabian Nights, and her nostrils tautened to the drift of perfume from funny little cubbyholes in the very walls of the *souk*. She peered into one of these tiny scent shops and was beckoned in by the perfume-seller, to have her wrist stroked with a little glass rod dipped into carnation and rose perfume, into orange-flower, jasmine and musk. The phials lay in dozens of little drawers, and she couldn't resist the temptation of a scent called Rapture of the Desert, and another for Maud.

The *souk* lay in a maze which brought her directly back to the hotel, and this time there were guests in the foyer, who greeted her with smiles and wished her a good morning in French or German. It seemed that these days British people came less often to the East, and she felt the young foreigner as she glanced into the restaurant to see if Maud had yet come down to breakfast.

Ah, there she was! Seated at the table they had shared at dinner last night, and in conversation with a young man Chrys had not seen before. He wore khaki trousers and a white shirt, tucked into a black leather belt that matched his kneeboots. When Maud spotted Chrys and waved, the man turned round and stared at her. He was about thirty and had a tanned face surmounted by hair so light it looked bleached.

Maud introduced him as Peter Dorn and said that he was already working at the diggings and that he had been a pupil of her husband's. He shook Chrys's hand and she was unsurprised when he spoke to her with a Dutch accent.

'This is very much a delightful surprise, Miss Devrel. When I heard that Maud had arrived at Beni Kezar with a new companion, well I did not expect to find that companion so—young.'

Maud grinned and invited him to stay and have breakfast with them. 'I don't doubt that you've already had rolls and coffee, but being a Dutchman, Peter, I'm sure you can put away some bacon and eggs.'

'I think I can.' He sat down beside Chrys, and she saw his nostrils flicker as he caught the aroma of the scents the Arab had applied to her skin. 'I will guess that you have been wandering in the *souk*, eh? And were enticed into one of those mysterious little perfumeries?'

'I couldn't resist buying something.' Chrys handed Maud a phial of scent across the table. 'Yours is called Garden of Carnations, Maud.'

'How nice of you, Chrys, to think of an old woman!' Maud immediately stroked the tiny glass rod against her throat. 'Mmmm, I'm now likely to get carried off to the tent of an amorous man of the desert.'

Chrys laughed, while she felt Peter Dorn gazing inquisitively at the Arabic lettering on her own phial of scent. 'Do you believe that rapture might be found in the desert, Miss Devrel?' His sky-blue eyes met hers and they were teasing and at the same time inquisitive.

'All I really hope to acquire is a sun tan, a good riding horse, and a little knowledge of how to dig for ancient relics,' she replied, giving him a very candid look without a hint of flirtation in it. He was a good-looking man, with virile forearms fleeced with blond hair, but Chrys looked as undisturbed as if he had been an elderly professor. When the waiter came to the table she asked Maud to order for her scrambled eggs, kidneys and toast. 'I'm ravenous after my explorations. One could spend a fortune in that *souk*. Such carpets! And some of that copper and pewter ware! Not to mention the handbags! All handmade and with something inimitable about them.'

'I will judge that you have had your first taste of

being fascinated by the East and its oriental witchery,' said Peter Dorn. 'Beware. It can cast spells over certain people, and they find themselves unable to break the spell. Have you yet seen the sun set over the desert sands?'

She shook her head. 'I must admit, mijhneer, that it's an experience to which I am looking forward with a great deal of interest. I have seen pictures of such sunsets, but I have not yet seen the reality. Is it as magical as I have heard?'

'Even more so—and may I call you by your first name? Is it Christine?'

'No, it's Chrys, spelled like the beginning of the flower.'

'Very nice. I like it.' He spoke with Dutch decision. 'You must allow me to find a good horse for you, and then you must allow me to show you your first sunset.'

'Thank you,' Chrys glanced at Maud. 'When shall we be making camp in the desert?'

'If Peter can help arrange matters with the local *kaid*, then I thought we might set up camp tomorrow. Today we could do some sight-seeing, and buy provisions, and have tea in the gardens of the mosque. What do you say, Chrys?'

'Marvellous!' Her eyes glowed, and the sun through the windows stroked the tawny-gold of her hair. She felt young and zestful, and that depression of the past few weeks had lifted suddenly from her spirits. Madame de Casenove had been right to urge her to come to the East. It was a place for forgetfulness, so far from familiar things, and with an underlying sense of mystery of which she had been conscious ever since setting foot on Eastern soil.

She tucked into her breakfast with youthful appetite, and was watched admiringly by the Dutchman. 'What a change to see a young woman enjoy her food these days,' he said to Maud. 'I thought they were all on strict diets to preserve their svelte figures.'

'Chrys is the energetic sort who burns off the spare inches. She was up with the lark this morning, and isn't one of your indolent creatures of glamour, Peter. That's why I wanted her for my companion. I can't stand the bored and primping sort, who scream at crawlies, and want men in attendance all the time.'

'Well, I shall be in attendance at the camp, but I hope you won't mind too much.' Peter Dorn's smile was charming, and not overbearingly sure of itself. 'I shall try to blend in with the background.'

'An Arab might succeed in that, but not a Dutchman,' drawled Maud. 'I have an idea Chrys and myself will quite enjoy having you around. I hoped, in fact, that you might be at the diggings, but wasn't sure if you had returned from Peru. How was it there?'

'Cold.' He gave an expressive shiver. 'I was glad to get to the desert, and was most pleased when I found your letter awaiting me here at the hotel. To work again with Malcolm's wife is always a pleasure.'

'You're gallant, Peter.' Maud bowed her head in acknowledgément of his compliment, both to herself and her late husband. 'You were always his favoured pupil ... ah, they were good days, and I think I travel so much these days in order to keep myself from being lonely.'

Maud and Peter talked about the days gone by, while Chrys drank her coffee and listened to them. He stayed at Beni Kezar all the morning, helping them to arrange

154

about porters to take their baggage to the camp site on the following day, and he also went with them to the *kaid*'s stables, where they hired their mounts and received official permission to use the waterhole at the camp site. Peter then had to get back to the dig and said regretfully that he wished he could spare the time to take tea with them that afternoon.

They watched him ride off, and Maud looked well pleased. 'I'm glad we have a European male at the camp,' she said. 'We shall sleep easier at night.'

'I had no idea that you had a few old-fashioned ideas, Maud.' Chrys spoke teasingly. 'I believed you were fully emancipated from the idea of male protection.'

'Oh, I can take care of myself,' Maud said at once. 'But I have with me on this trip a young and attractive girl who has already caught the eye of one of the local Sheiks.'

'Don't remind me!' Chrys tried to sound flippant, but now that Maud mentioned the man, she was glad herself that Peter Dorn would be on hand to look big, blond and masculine. 'I suppose I have to accept his blessed charm?'

'Just to be diplomatic, Chrys. Come along, we'll type him a polite note of thanks and arrange for a boy to deliver it to him.'

'But we don't know his name or address,' Chrys pointed out.

'The waiter will know. The one who brought the package to you.'

But it turned out that the waiter didn't know, for he was a new employee at the hotel and had not been resident before at Beni Kezar, so it seemed like fate that

Chrys should have to accept the Hand of Fatma without even a word of thanks for it.

'*Mektub, mektub,*' said Maud philosophically.

When later on they drove to the mosque gardens for tea, the sky was clear, unclouded blue and the air was as heady and dazzling as great sips of champagne. Chrys leaned forward in the *arabeah* and filled her eyes with all the passing scenery, crowned by the great palms, which all seemed to take a natural *salaam* above the heads of the people, and the line of camels marching solemnly in the direction of the desert, loads of bedding and pots swaying on their backs, the women and children walking among them while the men rode high on the humps.

'What a typical sign of male superiority!' said Chrys scornfully.

'Not really.' Maud looked at her companion with twinkling eyes. 'The camel is a truculent beast and they need firm guidance or they'd dash off like hares with all those Bedouin belongings heading for Timbuctoo. They aren't too comfortable to sit, which is another reason why the women much prefer to walk. See how gracefully they walk! Being curled up on the neck of a camel would spoil that posture of theirs, and they know it. Can you hear the bells on their ankles? These women are the most feminine in the world, and they often choose quite deliberately to wear that one-eyed veil.'

'So in the East, what one sees is not always the obvious truth.' Chrys gazed after the Bedouin women in their long indigo blue robes, with a lilt to their walk and a magical sort of music at their heels. 'Maud, it must take years to come to terms with the contradictions of these people!'

'Of course, my dear. You won't learn everything in a mere matter of weeks. Did you like Peter?'

'He's charming, but aren't you afraid, Maud, that I shall lose my head over him?'

'Somehow I don't see it happening. Two fair people rarely click, for nature has a positive love of opposites.' And to bear out her statement, when they reached the gardens Maud took Chrys to see all the varied plants and flowers, growing in a profusion that took licence from the sun. The petunias, the gold and red nasturtiums, starry violet jasmine, and peonies like flame in contrast to the huge white geraniums, and sheets of purple bougainvillaea.

The sun picked out glittering motes in the bright tiles of the forecourt of the white mosque. Pigeons strutted on the stone coping of the fountains, and the drowsy perfume of the flowers mingled with that of the water against the hot stone.

Chrys felt again as if she had wandered into the Arabian Nights, and almost hypnotic was the sound of the cicadas hidden like leaves among the juniper and cypress trees.

This was not prayer time, so they were allowed into the lower hall of the mosque, with its painted panels like Persian carpets, and its marble-tiled floor, and cupola-arched doorways. A sigh was like a whisper, a whisper was like a shout, and the air was filled with an essence of musk and sandalwood and crushed jasmine petals.

They were served with tea and cakes beneath a giant fig tree, which stretched its branches and hung its great leaves like a green parasol above them.

'It's all very beautiful,' Chrys murmured. 'Achingly so.'

'Wait until you see the magnificent loneliness of the desert ... that will really set your imagination soaring. It's an added blessing that you can ride.'

'I learned when I was younger, but I haven't done much riding in the past few years. A dancer has to take care of her legs.'

'I daresay,' said Maud drily. 'It wouldn't look exactly artistic to see a bow-legged ballet dancer. Missing your old haunts yet?'

'No, they all seem strangely far away.' Chrys caught her breath. 'I think the lure of the East has come upon me, Maud. I thought I could be cool and distant towards all this, but suddenly I feel like a moth caught up in the threads of a gaudy web. I'm sunstruck, overwhelmed, and too entranced to struggle for my freedom. The sensation is dreamlike ... shall I wake in a while and find myself alone in the flat I shared with Dove?'

'Do you want to?' Maud studied the face of Chrys beneath the shifting green light of the fig leaves.

Chrys considered the question and then shook her head. 'While I had my dancing I had all I needed. But now—now I have become vulnerable like other lonely people. I believe the East calls to the lonely at heart.'

'It does, Chrys, and you are sensitive enough to realise it.'

'You have no more doubts, Maud, about bringing me here?' Chrys spoke seriously. 'I don't want to be a liability. I'll wear that floppy hat, even dress like a boy, if it will make me seem less—alien to the Arabs.'

'I don't think,' drawled Maud, 'that it will be thought quite proper if a young boy is seen in the double tent, especially at night. Arabs have a rather salacious sense of humour. No, things should be quite safe with Peter Dorn at the dig.'

They took a final stroll around the lovely gardens before driving home to the hotel. While Maud paid the driver Chrys stood and gazed at the sky, where the sun seemed to be smouldering away in a fountain of colour and flame. She visualised the sands of the desert bathed in that riot of colour, barbarous and yet beautiful, and the image quickened her breath and made her lips part ... almost as if ready to receive a kiss. She was looking like that as a car came to a halt at the corner of the square, in front of one of the old, shuttered-looking Arab houses that faced the hotel. Three men emerged from the limousine and made their way to the huge, nail-studded door of the house. Each man was robed, and walked with that feline grace so apparent in some of the Arabian people. Dignity and aloofness matched that grace, and as Chrys glanced across the road one of the men turned a moment and looked directly at her, standing there in her pale dress in the rich dying light of the sun.

It was no mistake, the height, the stance, and the gleam of a high red boot under the great cloak. He even seemed to incline his covered head slightly, and she pictured a smile curling on the well-cut lips under the black moustache.

Then the great door of the Arabian house was opened and the trio of men disappeared into the courtyard, with its glimpses of a fountain and the tall silhouettes of palm trees. Then the door closed, but Chrys

159

had the disquieting feeling that eyes gazed at her through the narrow iron grille in the door, and she felt them to be mocking and dangerously persistent as the eyes of a tiger stalking its prey.

She was glad to escape into the hotel with Maud, but when she was alone in her room she picked up the little Hand of Fatma as if compelled and felt in that moment a strange sense of fatalism. He had sent her the charm to let her know they would meet again, out there in the desert, and she was faced with the decision to remain at Beni Kezar, or make some excuse to Maud and catch the late train back to civilisation, where men in picturesque robes did not make silent and subtle threats which seemed to sway a girl between flight and fury.

She stood there in the darkening room, the charm clenched in her hand, and she knew that a confrontation with him was inevitable if she entered the desert, the great gold garden, where menace and enticement threw their shadows across the sands.

She would throw this charm in his face and tell him to go to the devil ... she would tell him scornfully that she wasn't remotely interested in becoming an inmate of his *harem*!

Despite this resolve Chrys awoke the following morning with a knot of tension at the base of her stomach, so that she couldn't eat and drank cups of coffee for her breakfast. She and Maud were setting out early so they wouldn't lose the first coolness of the day and arrive at the camp in the heat of the sun. Chrys was presented with the floppy-brimmed hat which was meant to hide the brightness of her hair, and as she put it on and pulled the brim down over her left eye, she reflected that it was a pity she hadn't been wearing the hat at the railway station, along with her plain shirt and pale brown riding trousers.

'Well, will I pass as a member of a desert dig?' She grinned at Maud, and betrayed not a hint of her nervous excitement, which the coffee had stirred up instead of settled.

The older woman studied her and looked quizzical. 'I'm afraid you'd look beguiling in a sack, Chrys. That old hat of mine looks dashing and sort of Garboish on you, and those trousers never looked that good on a boy.'

So they set out on this clear and beckoning morning, riding the horses which they had hired from the *kaid*, with their porters and loaded camels following on behind. Chrys glanced behind her and was fascinated by those long-necked animals, with a leather thong fastened into a nose ring so the driver, seated way up on the powerful humped back, could guide his beast and be master of its truculent disposition.

Soon they had left behind them the old, sun-burned walls of the town and outcrops of rock appeared, breaking through the sand like bare white bone, with scrub-mimosa flowering here and there to make a bright splash of colour.

Hills rose against the dazzling blue sky like the battlements of old ruined castles, and the breeze that blew across the peachy-coloured sand was filled with a tang of wild, unknown places. The jingle and rustle of the harness was pleasant on the morning air, for the hooves of the animals were muffled by the sand, so that they seemed to be gliding across velvet itself.

They passed a few quiet Bedouin encampments, wherever a small stream flowed among a group of palm trees, where the low black tents were pitched, curtained at one end and wide open at the other, where the cooking fires were built, and where the gold-skinned children played among the goats and the small herds of *mouflon*, the little sheep like balls of wool, and often the only means of support for these rambling gipsy-like families. The black sheep among them wore strings of blue glass beads, Chrys noticed. They were obviously 'lambs of Satan' and needed extra protection from the evil eye.

The tall women in their homespun dresses, clad like Ruth and Rachel, filled their fat-bellied waterjars at the stream, and Chrys wondered what it was like to be always a tent-dweller, wandering from oasis to oasis, and bearing with a patient smile the extremes of hot and cold weather, the primitive conditions of being a wife and a mother many miles from the civilised comforts of a city woman's life.

As Chrys rode by on her Arab horse, obviously a girl despite her masculine attire, the Bedouin women gazed after her, and they probably wondered what her life was like. She smiled at them, but they considered her with gravity, as if she were even more strange to them than they could ever be to her. And they were right! The desert was their proper background, into which they blended with a rugged, biblical grace. She in her trousers and brimmed hat must seem to them a peculiar species of womanhood.

When the last encampment was left behind, the horses and their riders, and the laden camels, were engulfed in the silence of the rolling sands, turning to white-gold as the sun rose higher and cast its brilliant hot light down over the desert. The heat of the day was beginning, like a cloak of saffron silk, heavy and clinging as it touched the skin. Chrys became aware of the heat like gloves on her hands as she held the reins of her mount, and the back of her shirt clung against her shoulders. She was glad of the brimmed hat, shielding her untried eyes from the ashen blaze of the sand.

How far away was England and all that had happened there to bring her to this desert. She looked about her, and it was real and not a mirage. The heat and the shimmer of the sands were a living reality and she was a part of it all. She sat upon the red saddle of a grey Arab horse, and was surrounded by a sea of molten gold, sculptured sometimes into the shape of waves ... glowing and relentless, a place to be lost in without a guide, who sat high on his camel, a pattern of heart-shaped hoof marks left in the sand behind them.

They stopped to drink tea and to eat jammy doughnut puffs in the shade of some rocks, and Maud asked her how she was enjoying her first encounter with the desert.

Chrys looked at Maud and the answer lay in her eyes. In the shadow of the hat's brim they were intensely blue; the magic of it all was trapped in her eyes like a little flame. 'It's tormenting and it's wonderful,' she said. 'It's like nothing else I've ever known.'

'You don't find it monotonous?' Maud gave her a very direct look over the rim of her mug of tea. 'It must all seem very different from the colour and enchantment of your world of ballet. Ballet was more real to you than real life, so you told me, and now you have seen the primitive desert-dwellers, and the black tents they live and die in, living a life in which theatres and gaiety play no part.'

'In the difference of it all lies the fascination.' Chrys gazed around at the couched camels, and the porters with their lean faces and fierce eyes that were falcon-like in their quickness and their regard, their feet as tensile as their hands and tanned to the shade of leather. Chrys hugged her mug of tea, and felt as if all the secrets of the silent desert were being slowly revealed for her.

'Seduction isn't true love,' Maud murmured. 'You might look at it all next week and wish yourself on the steamer home.'

Chrys smiled and shook her head, for confidence was suddenly spreading through her like a weed, strangling any last-minute doubts she had about venturing into the Garden of Allah. The desert all around them had become a dazzling ocean of gold, but she was no longer afraid of what it held in store for her.

She crumbled the remnants of a doughnut and threw the crumbs into the shade of a rock. Tiny azure birds flew down on them, making a cawing sound ... despite the hawks of the desert the blue birds still came and made it their home. Perky and pretty, they pecked at the crumbs, bright specks of chestnut on their little backs.

'I think, Maud, that in some ways my training in ballet has prepared me for the desert life. The dance demands a spartan régime and loads of stamina and soul. Even applause cannot spoil a ballerina, for she knows that early the next morning she must be at the *barre*, training alongside the novice, and sweating every bit as hard to keep trim and supple and disciplined. Here in the desert I shall ride and dig and keep fit, but if I had taken a desk job for a year I dread to think of

164

the consequences! It is better for the legs to become a little bowed than for the ballet dancer's bottom to spread!'

Maud laughed and climbed to her feet. 'Come along, Pavlova. We've only about another hour's ride to the diggings, and I am sure Peter is impatient for our arrival. He'll get no end of a kick out of taking you on as a pupil, and you may even be lucky enough to find a Roman bowl.'

'I'd get a thrill out of that myself.' As Chrys swung into the saddle of her horse she felt not a twinge of pain from her back injury and was certain today that fortune smiled on her, almost as warmly as the desert sun.

The porters urged their grumbling camels to their feet, and Chrys half-turned in the saddle to watch the men tuck their bare feet around the long necks of the animals. Bells jingled on the harness of the camels, and the *djellabas* of the men were stark white against the shaggy buff coats. The *cheche* of one of the men was draped almost like a mask across his face, and she felt the glitter of his eyes as he caught her looking at him. At once she looked away from him, and cantered her horse to catch up with Maud.

But as she rode along she was distinctly aware of that rider high on his camel saddle behind her. It was instinctive with her to notice grace of movement, and that particular porter had mounted his animal with long-legged movements of peculiar grace, and up there on that high saddle he didn't slouch but sat there as proudly as a prince.

Her heart jarred strangely in her side. Her thoughts flew over the sands, over the water, to a terrace above the Thames, where she had danced with a man whose movements had been as animal and supple as those of the Arab riding in the wake of her horse. He too had been masked, and she wondered if he was still enjoying the night spots of London, or whether he had yet returned to his house called *Belle Tigresse*.

She felt the quick beating of her heart as she rode along, and fought the odd compulsion to glance again at the porter behind her. Surely it was coincidental that a movement of the body, a turn of the head, a flick of the eyes, had reminded her of a man she would far sooner forget? Surely it was a flash of the old anger that made her blood run fast through her veins! They had parted with bare civility. He had clicked his heels and gone out of her life.

'Beware of melting when you reach the desert,' he had said, in that taunting way of his. 'And if you do melt, be sure you are in the correct pair of arms.'

'There is one thing for sure,' she had retorted. 'They will never be *your* arms.'

'Perhaps not,' he agreed. 'But on the other hand there is an old Arab saying to the effect that the most unlikely thing to happen is nearly always the thing that does happen.'

It was those words, and the tiny mocking smile at the edge of his mouth, which haunted Chrys and made her look twice at every man she saw out here, seeing in the slightest gesture a resemblance which probably never existed at all.

She restrained herself from looking round and prodded her mount to catch up with Maud's. Probably eager to reach the Roman diggings where she had last searched for coins and relics alongside her husband,

Maud had given her mount quite a bit of rein and they had forged well ahead of Chrys when all of a sudden she saw the horse shy wildly at something across his path. The long forelegs threshed the air, and the next instant Maud was flung half out of the saddle, with her right foot holding her in the stirrup as the horse bolted in fright across the hot sands.

Chrys gave a cry of alarm and gave rein to her own mount in an atempt to catch up with the bolting horse. She was terrified for Maud, who looked in grave danger of being badly hurt if suddenly flung from the saddle.

Fleet as her mount was, something flashed past on long thundering legs and with loping strides soon shortened the distance between itself and the frightened animal that was dragging Maud as if she were a puppet. The camel and its rider were soon ahead of the horse, and swerving skilfully in front of it they brought it to a standstill, head hanging and flanks heaving, its rider still at a painful angle, caught by her foot in the twisted stirrup.

As Chrys galloped towards the group, she saw the rider of the camel kneel his animal, dismount swiftly and make for the figure of Maud. He gentled the horse, and was lifting Maud from its back as Chrys rode up to them and leapt from her own saddle.

She ran forward, crying Maud's name. The man who had saved her turned his head to look at Chrys, and the *cheche* blew from his face, and eyes of a most unusual grey looked into the wild blue eyes of Chrys, and she was shocked, and at the same time too con-cerned for Maud to even speak his name as she stepped forward to where he had placed the shaken, perhaps injured woman, holding her so that she rested in the crook of his arm.

Maud winced painfully as Chrys knelt beside her. 'Hurts like the devil!' She gestured at her right foot. 'Mustn't blame the horse. I think a *jerboa* darted in front of him and startled him. I didn't grab the reins tightly enough and he was up and away. Lucky my foot caught and held me, but I—I think it's twisted.'

'Allow me, *madame*. I shall try not to add to your pain.' A lean hand emerged from the full sleeve of the spotless robes and the fingers passed briefly over Maud's ankle, causing her to bite down on her lip even at so gentle a touch. 'I fear the stirrup may have crushed a small bone, *madame*.' The smoke-grey eyes that did not belong to an Arab porter gazed into Maud's eyes. 'It is essential that you see a doctor as soon as possible, and as it would not be possible for you to ride back to Beni Kezar, and there is not a doctor at your camp, I suggest that you allow me to take you to my house. I have a geologist friend in residence there who is also a qualified doctor, and it is not such a long ride as the one back to town.'

Maud was staring at him, absorbing his excellent English, and his lean but not Arab face with sheer amazement. Chrys at the other side of her watched the exchange of looks, and knew exactly what was passing through Maud's mind. *Who on earth was this handsome devil who spoke like a gentleman instead of a porter?*

'Maud, I had better introduce you.' Chrys looked at him then, and there was a wry little smile on her lips. 'This is the Prince Anton de Casenove, who has a predilection for masks and subtle games, and I can tell

168

you now that he has been following us around since the first moment we arrived at Port Said. The moustache fooled me, because when last we met he was clean-shaven, and I had not yet seen how Arab clothing can be a disguise in itself. In London the Prince wore the smartest tailoring from Savile Row, and I suppose if I expected to see him out here, I expected the same suave apparel, not *un arabe* from his head-ropes to his Moroccan leather boots!'

'This is——' Maud shook her head in bewilderment. 'This is really too much for me in my shocked state. A Prince?'

'Quite so, *madame*.' He inclined his head and a slight smile flickered on his lips. 'Miss Devrel and I knew each other in London. But if she had known that I was coming to this part of the desert she would have gone to Timbuctoo in order to avoid me. My wicked sense of humour could not resist a little masquerade, but as things turned out it was a good thing I was on hand today. The camel and I were useful, eh?'

'Much more than useful, *m'sieur*.' Maud gave him a deeply grateful look. 'I couldn't have held on to those reins much longer, and if I'd gone under those hooves —well, by now I'd be in paradise, or the other place. Thank you, young man, but all the same I think we ought to press on to camp. Perhaps your doctor could come to me there——?'

'It would be much more comfortable for you at my house, *madame*.' He spoke firmly. 'Already that ankle is much swollen, and you are still very much shaken by your experience. I definitely think that you and your companion should come with me to *Belle Tigresse*. In fact I am going to insist that you do so.'

'Are you indeed?' Maud looked at him with obstinacy, and a touch of the alarm which he automatically inspired. Chrys was still feeling annoyed that he had fooled her, but desperately glad that he had been on hand to divert a really bad accident. She kept silent, for this must be decided between Maud and Anton. The battle of wills was theirs this time, and as she knelt there she felt the sun striking down hot against her head, and she realized that during her race to catch up with Maud's horse the hat had blown from her head. She put up a hand and pushed the tawny hair from her brow, which was beaded with fine sweat. She felt the flick of Anton's eyes, over her hair, her face, and the boyish shirt and trousers which she wore. She refused to meet his grey and devilish eyes ... but somewhere inside her a little flame was leaping.

She was furious with him, and she wanted to tell him just what she thought of him for that game he had played on the train, pretending to be a mysterious Sheik in pursuit of her! The mortifying part was that he had succeeded so well in making her feel that she was in danger of her virtue!

How she longed to pay him back ... later on ... when he wasn't quite the hero of the hour.

'And why do you think you can give me orders?' Maud demanded of him, speaking the words through lips that were drawn with pain. 'Because you probably saved my life, eh?'

'No, *madame*.' He gave her his most charmingly sardonic smile. 'Because *Belle Tigresse* is a rather lonely house these days, and it would welcome both of you. Also it will be more comfortable for you than a tent in the desert, for you can take it from me that you have more wrong with your foot than a mere twist of the ligaments. You are in bad pain, I can see that.'

'It is rather sickening,' Maud admitted. She glanced at Chrys. 'Well, what do you say, my child? You're kneeling there without saying a word, but I'm sure you're thinking quite a lot. Do we accept the Prince's invitation?'

Chrys wanted to cry out that it was the last thing she wanted them to do, but the pallor of Maud's face and the obvious distress in her eyes made her say quietly: 'I think it would be only sensible, Maud. You will be well cared for there, and made comfortable. I—perhaps I could go on to the camp site. Peter will be there——'

'That is the very reason why you cannot go there, Miss Devrel.' The Prince broke in on her words, not harshly but in a voice as smooth as silk. 'The *kaid* would be most displeased if he knew that a young man and a young woman were sharing alone a camping site which he has put at the disposal of Mrs Christie. I am afraid that desert etiquette goes against your obvious desire to be alone with Mr Dorn. If Mrs Christie comes to stay at *Belle Tigresse*, then you must accompany her, and you have already agreed that it will be to her best advantage to be my guest while her foot is mending.'

In the silence which followed his words, that little flame of fury leapt higher in Chrys, while Maud's head drooped against the robed arm of Anton. Chrys swallowed the angry words that leapt to her lips, the hot denial that she 'desired to be all alone with Peter Dorn' and instead she agreed to go with Maud to his desert house.

171

They went on horseback, the thin and now rather feverish figure of Maud held firmly in the saddle in front of Anton, her head at rest against his robed shoulder. The porter and the two camels followed on behind, and the sun was like a golden blaze in the sky when the white walls of the house rose against the tawny sweep of the sands, the green fronds of gigantic palm trees shading the dome of it, and the courtyard beyond its arched entrance.

CHAPTER NINE

IT was such an unexpected house, all alone like this in the midst of the golden sands, and so fascinating with its dome of coloured glass over the central courtyard, so that the sun was filtered down in a myriad jewel colours, and the rampant tropic vegetation took on a mysterious jungle look, and curtained everything of stone or marble with a cloak of flame and purple and rich cream flower. Scents were trapped here, and the kick and scrape of cicadas, not to mention the lizards that lay stone still or scuttled dragon-green across the tiles.

Chrys had come out from the cool hall, drawn by the fascination of this jungly courtyard, the colours playing over her white shirt and her pale skin as she drew breath and absorbed the relief of leaving Maud in the capable hands of Doctor Ben Omair.

The master of the house had gone off to acquaint Peter Dorn with details of the mishap, and as Chrys wandered about and explored this amazing patio, she wondered exactly what he would say to the young Dutchman. She hoped that Peter would be allowed to come here. He was so blond and big and solid that he would dilute the exotic atmosphere of this place and dispel some of the heady magic with a hearty breath of common sense.

She mounted some shallow curving steps into another part of the house, and found herself walking beneath dark cedar beams, between ivory-white walls, and upon a massive carpet of mellowed colours. Here in this long cool room were squat coffee tables with mother-of-pearl inlay, low divans covered with wonderful old prayer rugs, and graceful, jewelled, lethal scimitars attached to the walls. There were also lances, and some fine old horse pieces. And there were books, massed on cedarwood shelves, of all sizes, and in a variety of languages, with bindings of deep-toned leather.

A man's room! Redolent of an aromatic smoke that clung to the pages of the well-read books ... and to the robes in which the Prince had dressed himself in order to fool her into thinking she was being pursued by one of the local Sheiks.

Darn him! She glared at a jewelled scimitar, as if she would have liked to do him an injury with it. And then a reluctant smile touched her lips as she sank down on a thick animal pelt and took a delicious sweet from a hammered box on a nearby table. She lay back on the pelt—not knowing it to be that of a Siberian tiger—and her teeth crunched the nut buried in the thick chocolate.

Her gaze roved about this room that was such a

173

mixture of the strongly masculine and the subtly sensuous, and she imagined him here taking coffee, clad in one of those monkish *haiks*, those narrow, adroit feet clasped in thonged sandals.

In London she had thought him the most worldly man she had ever met ... now suddenly she was confronted by a more primitive side to him, all the more disturbing because the man was so educated, and at the same time so unafraid to do the crazy, maddening things that tamer men never even thought of. Chrys tried to picture Dove's husband in any other role but that of the devoted, time-keeping, candid young lover, and she smiled, and realized that in Dove's shoes right now she would have been hopelessly bored.

She listened to the hot, humming silence that lay over *Belle Tigresse* as she lay, too languorous to stir, on the furry pelt that was longer than her own figure. She let her eyelids fall slowly like shutters over her sun-tired eyes, and she wriggled her feet out of her shoes. Mmmm, it felt good to relax after all the tensions of the morning ... she would stay here awhile, in the restfulness of this shadowy room, and then she would go and see how Maud was feeling.

And there on the pelt Chrys fell fast asleep, her tawny hair mixing with the tawny fur, emotionally worn out and secure in the knowledge that Maud was in good hands.

She slept dreamlessly for some time, and awoke quite suddenly to find herself in strange surroundings, and aware that she was being scrutinised. Her eyes flew open, and there in the light of a lamp, booted feet deep in the carpet, wide cloak held back by an arm crooked on his hip, stood Prince Anton. She swept the tousled hair back from her eyes, and knew instantly that she must look childish. She started to scramble to her feet, and immediately he took her by the shoulders and brought her to her feet quite close to him.

Still bemused from her nap, she looked at him without knowing quite what to say. Although close to her, he seemed a stranger in his Arab clothes, and the line of his moustache made him look so ruthless. It was as if he had left the civilised part of him back in London, discarded with his Savile Row suits and his *savoir faire*.

'It did not take you long to find my private sanctum,' he said. 'I wonder if some strange instinct led you to it? We are all creatures of instinct, you know, and here in the desert the primitive senses come close to the surface of ourselves and that is why for a while the newcomer feels as if he or she had quaffed a little too much champagne. Do you feel heady, a little dizzy, and yet tensely aware of the slightest sound, the smallest movement, the softest flutter of bird wing or petal?'

He described so exactly how she felt that Chrys would have lied if she had denied his description. His very touch on her shoulders was so acute as to resemble a pain.

'I suppose you're vastly amused that I didn't guess it was you on the train?' she said, her head thrown back so she could look at his face. 'You have a strange sense of humour, *milor*. I suppose the Hand of Fatma was meant to warn me that your hand was reaching out to me? What is it you want of me ... the usual melting heap of womanhood at your feet?'

He quirked an eyebrow, and the edge of his moustache seemed to quirk as well. 'If you are going to be a guest in my house, then there is one thing you must know from the start. I am not addicted to the usual, and much prefer the unusual. Secondly although you are now in the *seraglio* of my house, meaning the part where women are not normally allowed, there is no *harem* at *Belle Tigresse*, and the only woman on the premises apart from Mrs Christie and yourself is the housekeeper. If you are reassured that I won't suddenly demand your presence in the master bedroom, attended by eunuchs who will force you into my arms, then it might be possible for you to enjoy your stay without too much strain on your valued and closely guarded independence.'

'Did you see Peter Dorn?' Her cheeks had flushed at his sardonic summing up of the needling little fears she did feel as a reluctant guest under his roof. It was a large house, a fantastic collection of rooms screened by *meshrebiya* balconies, roofs and flights of steps seen through copings of stone sculpture, walled enclosures, wooden doors draped in pale jasmine and deep violet plumbago.

There might well be a secluded wing to which no one went but this man in his picturesque robes, seeking the pleasures of which she had only a misty awareness. Although in ballet she had danced in the strong arms of warm, lithe partners, she was curiously innocent of what men really thought and desired.

There lay in the eyes of Anton de Casenove a thousand answers to any questions she might have asked, but she felt there would always be a part of him that was secluded and not to be known. The smoky beauty of his eyes, the black and screening lashes, the little stabs of mockery, all were aimed at shaking her youthful poise. He saw right through her with those worldly eyes, but there were depths to him, secrets known to him, which made her head spin.

He was really a thorough wretch, she told herself, as if all the time he inwardly laughed at her and planned her seduction. As the lean, sun-browned fingers pressed the fine bones at the base of her neck, she sought wild refuge in the Dutchman.

'What did Peter say about the accident? Will you allow him to come and visit Maud?'

'I would not dream of depriving either of you of a visit from him,' Anton drawled. 'I don't want a frustrated young tigress prowling around my house, ready to fly at me with tooth and claw. He will come tomorrow for lunch. For myself, as I have been riding the hot sands, I feel in need of some tea. You will join me in the courtyard, but I am sure that first you would like to go and change into a dress. It would be cooler, and far more attractive than the riding trousers.'

As it happened she felt like a change of clothing, so she didn't argue with him. She also fancied a cup of tea, out there under the cool greenery and the trailing flowers. She glanced at her wristwatch and was amazed to see how the time had fled.

'Come, I will show you to your apartment,' he said. 'In time you will grow accustomed to the house, but at first it can bewilder the stranger. Arabian houses are built rather like old English castles, so that one can always find a place to hide, but can very easily go astray.'

With an imperious sweep of his cloak he led her from his own quarters and along corridors, up sudden flights of steps, and around unexpected corners of this odd and fascinating house until he paused outside an oval shaped vermilion door and opened it for her.

'I shall be in the courtyard when you are ready,' he said. 'One of Hazra's children will be sent to wait for you here in the corridor, to see that you don't lose your way.'

'Thank you, but who is Hazra?' Chrys stood in the frame of the vermilion door and looked up at him; the boots and robes and rope-bound head-covering made him very tall and imposing, and she saw again how easy it had been to mistake him for an Arab. The dense brows, the strongly etched cheekbones, and that devilish black moustache all added to the illusion. She felt quite sure that the years he had spent in the East had almost made him an Arab at heart. He seemed to exude the very breath of the desert through his bronzed skin, and the very light of the sky seemed to glitter in his eyes.

'She is my housekeeper.' With a mocking inclination of his head he swung on his booted heel and strode off, taking it arrogantly for granted that Chrys would obey his orders without a murmur. What was so annoying was that she could really do nothing else but obey them. She couldn't ask for a pot of tea to be brought to her room because she didn't know the language, and she was simply dying for a cup!

She withdrew into the rooms which were to be hers while she remained a guest at *Belle Tigresse*, and she saw that her suitcases had been placed on an ottoman at the foot of the carved bed, draped in clouds of almond-pale netting. The bleached walls of the room were like rough silk to the hand, and the furniture was darkly ornate, while the windows were set within richly carved wooden cages, through which in days gone by

178

the women of the household would have looked without being seen. A wonderful old lantern, fitted with panes of coloured glass, hung between the windows, and there were painted cupboards, carved brackets on the walls filled with copper ornaments, and over the floor lay one of the fabulous Eastern carpets, teeming with warm colour and a thousand intricate designs.

Beyond the bedroom lay a smaller room, less ornate, with a divan and a little carved table, and a shelf of books. And beyond that was the bathroom, and Chrys stood speechless in the doorway, both amazed and a trifle shocked by the black marble bathtub that was sunk into the floor, with chiselled nymphs decorating the huge mirror, and a leopard skin across the black and white tiles.

After her first breathless moments of adjustment to such luxury, Chrys felt an irresistible urge to wallow in that tub and let her cares go by.

But *he* would be waiting, and he was impetuous and impatient enough to come charging up here in search of her if she did not appear for tea. She had to make do with a cool splash at the pyramid wash-basin, and after spraying herself with cologne she took a pale blue, shake-out dress from her suitcase and zipped herself into it. She brushed her hair until it crackled and shone, dashed lipstick across her mouth, and noticed how large and deep her eyes looked as she took a glance at herself in the wall-mirror.

She looked like Alice in Wonderland, she thought, but there just wasn't time to do adult things to her hair, so leaving it to swing free on her shoulders she left her apartment and went out into the corridor. She glanced around for this child who was to take her

179

downstairs to the courtyard, and her gaze fell instead upon a slim creature in a dress of coloured stripes, whose long black hair was pinned back in slides, and whose eyes were the colour of dark honey set round with long black lashes. In her earlobes hung small gold hoops, and her narrow feet were bare below the rather long hem of her dress.

She and Chrys stared at each other, one so fair, the other so dark, with a skin of warm, flawless amber and rather full lips.

'Are you Hazra?' said Chrys, for to her mind this was no child but a young woman, and Prince Anton had said that only his housekeeper, apart from Maud and herself, shared this house with him in the capacity of a woman.

'I am Saffida, and the *sidi* has asked me to conduct Mademoiselle to the courtyard.' The girl spoke in French, with a soft and attractive accent, and behind her heavy lashes she was studying Chrys with an un-childlike curiosity.

Chrys looked at Saffida and felt a stab of scorn that Anton should call her a *child*. The girl was a raving little beauty, with centuries of Eastern love lore running in her veins.

'Are you Hazra's daughter?' Chrys broke into a rather dry smile. 'I was expecting someone much smaller and younger.'

'I have very much grown since the *sidi* was last here.' The girl's full lips made a sort of bee-stung movement. 'I am now ready for marriage.'

'At what age,' asked Chrys, 'does the marriage of an Arabian girl take place?'

'At fourteen, if she has sufficient dowry.'

'You are more than that, surely?'

'I am sixteen, *mademoiselle*, and the *sidi* will provide my dowry.'

'That is very generous of him, Saffida.'

'Is it not the custom in your own land?'

'Well, not exactly.' Chrys glanced at the girl as they stepped out of a sculptured doorway into the coins of sunlight tumbling down through the feathery branches of some pepper trees. 'In England the father usually pays for the wedding——'. There she broke off as Prince Anton stepped from among the trees, bare-headed now, and clad in a slash-throated tunic of grey silk, with narrow black trousers and sandals with a leather thong holding them to his feet.

'Ah, so there you are! *Merci, mon enfant*,' he said to the Arabian girl, slanting a smile that held not a hint of flirtation. In answer to his smile Saffida placed her slim hands together and gave him a graceful, feminine version of the *salaam*. Her lashes fluttered and her golden ear hoops caught the sunlight. Then she turned and walked silently on her bare narrow feet, showing the heels that were hennaed.

'What a very pretty *child*,' said Chrys. 'I was expecting a gamine and found myself face to face with a sylph.'

'Was it a pleasant surprise?' he drawled, leading her to a wicker table set among the jasmine-draped trees, with deep wicker armchairs at either side of it. He drew out one of the chairs and Chrys had to walk close to him in order to sit down in the chair. She felt tangibly the masculine strength and warmth of him, the casual mockery, and the princely magnetism. As she sat down that magnetism seemed to cause a strand of her hair to cling against him. She felt him take the strand in his fingers and though he did no more than stroke it back against her neck, she felt as if he touched the entire surface of her skin and left it tingling.

She was glad when he sat down in the opposite chair, sprawling his long legs across the tiles, and taking the ease of a tiger in the sun. Even his eyes held a lazy smoulder as they watched her pour the tea from the long spout of the silver pot into the cups of pale china stamped with tiny coronets.

She handed him his cup and saucer, and then sat back with her own, half closing her eyes with the relish of the tea.

'It is good, eh?' he murmured. 'Especially when the throat is dry.'

As always there seemed a double meaning to his words, but she chose not to take any notice, though she felt the faint quivering of her nerves as she sat there with him, among the angel's trumpet with its flared blossoms, the henna and saffron plants, and the great clumps of roses.

'Did you know that in the days of the Arab lords these courtyards were made for the woman?' He leaned forward to take a coconut cake from the silver dish. He bit into it with his white teeth, and he kept on looking at her with those smoky eyes, and she could smell the scent of the camphor trees, and there was a coloured facet dancing on the leaves ... like the dancing, dangerous light in his grey eyes.

'It's a beautiful courtyard,' she said. 'It must evoke for you, *milor*, a pleasant image of all those lovely women of the *harem*.'

'Does it not evoke for you an image of their master?' he drawled.

'Perhaps.' She shrugged carelessly. 'An enormous

man, I think, with jewelled fingers and a rumbling laugh, and one of those spade beards with a dash of silver in it.'

'And how would you have felt about being his— guest?'

'Quite safe, I'm certain. I'm not opulent enough to make a very desirable candidate for the *harem*.'

'Come, you thought quite the reverse on the train, and I should have relished seeing your face, *chérie*, when you were presented with the Hand of Fatma from a man whom you thought to be one of the local Sheiks.'

Chrys glared at him. 'It was all very amusing, wasn't it? But not quite such fun for poor Maud. I'm only here for her sake. I'd give anything to be elsewhere.'

'With the big Dutchman, no doubt?'

'Yes! He hasn't the *droit du seigneur* attitude towards women that you have! A girl can talk with him in a friendly way, without the constant worry that he will do something unexpected. You, *milor*! Why, it's like taking tea with a tiger!'

He laughed lazily. 'So I set you on edge, eh? You don't know from one moment to the next what to expect from me. I wonder what you are expecting right now? I can see how tensed you are, and yet I am doing my best to play the kind and generous host.'

'Your generosity is only matched by your despotism!' The words broke from her lips and would not be controlled . . . it was almost as if she were driven to provoke him, but when she saw the narrowing of his eyelids over the glitter of his eyes, the rigid tensing of his forearm muscles, and the flare of his nostrils, she knew that she had gone too far. For an electrifying second they stared at each other, and then he had loomed to his feet and thrusting aside his armchair he came to where she sat and without ceremony he yanked her to her feet.

'I have been as patient with you as I intend to be. I have taken from you the final insolence! You little dancing girl!' His fist held her hair so that when she tried to wrench herself away from him the painful tug at the roots of her hair drove her back against him. She felt his hard bare chest under the tunic, and she looked up at him wildly and saw the raw little flames in his eyes a moment before he tipped her over his arm and forcibly kissed her.

She wanted not to feel a thing, but to be like cold stone in his arms, but instead, for an eternity of breathless, riotous, unimaginable seconds, she was lost ... lost to herself and to all the world outside and beyond this desert courtyard. He was brutal, and then he was indescribably warm and wanting. The desire to hurt and crush gave way to the keener pleasure of kissing her eyes, the backs of her ears, the soft curves of her neck, and her shoulders.

Something thudded close to her ribs, and the sensation was so pleasantly puzzling until she realised that it was his heart beating against her. It was then that her legs literally folded beneath her and with a low and throaty laugh he lifted her and carried her into the house, up a shallow flight of curving steps to the place he had called the *seraglio* ... mockingly, of course, but as always with an underlying hint of the truth.

'Call me tyrant again, you sand cat,' he growled against her earlobe.

'Let me go——' she pleaded, but the words had no strength, no reality, not the faintest desire to be obeyed.

'Is that really what you want, *dorogaya*?' His eyes were on her lips, studying them as if through smoky fire. 'I swear if I let you go those long white legs of yours will melt you at my feet, and that was always an attitude which you swore never to assume.'

'You've had too many women at your feet,' she said, and there was a tremor to her voice, and to look at him was to feel again the pang of almost intolerable pleasure which his lips on hers had awakened in her body. She had so wanted to be the one woman whom his touch did not disturb. She had wanted to be cool and unruffled, and able to walk out of his arms without a hair out of place.

Instead ... the contrast panicked her and she began to struggle in his arms. 'Anton, this has gone on long enough! Put me down!'

'If you say so.' He dropped her among the cushions of a divan, and then with that leopard-like grace of movement which she would recognise in a crowd of a thousand men, he knelt beside the divan and leaned towards her and his eyes were smoky-grey and drowsy, and there seemed an incoherent purr in his throat as he took her arm and ran his lips all the way to the crook of her elbow, where they stayed, warm as a flame against the smooth, soft skin.

' "O, hair of gold! O, crimson lips! O, face made for the luring and the love of man!" ' Only he could speak such words and make them alive and meaningful. 'Wilde was more the poet of love than Byron or Shelley. Don't you think so, my little sand cat?'

She gazed at him in the lamplight and there was a golden, barbaric quality to his looks in that moment. Cossack and prince, and man of the desert. She could feel the fascination of him stirring through her veins and the old desire to resist him awoke in her ... she must stop this before she became just another name on his list of conquests.

'You are very accomplished in the art of seduction, Anton. Have you plans for Saffida as well as for me, the cool English ballet dancer whom you swore would melt with your charm? Saffida is very pretty——'

'Saffida is a child,' he cut in, his eyes narrowing again to that steely glitter, striking across her face and her throat like a knife-edge. 'Your implication is not worthy of you, Chrysdova. The one thing above all which I admired in you was your integrity—do you think that I have not a scrap of it? Do you think me such a rake?'

His eyes searched hers, demanding an honest answer, and looking at him she was suddenly aware of all the nice things about him. Nice! The word shocked her in association with him, and yet there was an undeniable truth to it. Sometimes when he smiled ... ah, it was crazy to dwell on the attraction of him ... it was asking for a broken heart to let herself be drawn again into those warm, strong arms.

'You make toys of women,' she flung at him. 'While they please you everything is wonderful, but their very surrender makes it easy for you to say that all women are the same as your mother was. I won't be your toy! I won't be like them! I won't be made a fool of by those wicked and beguiling eyes of yours. I won't!'

She flung her hands over her own eyes, to shut out his face, and to hide the sudden tears that choked her. She heard him say her name in a roughly tender voice, and then she was pulled against him, her wet face was pressed to his chest and his hand was stroking her hair. 'No!' She pushed at him, and the bare skin of his chest was under her hand, and the shocking feel of the scar where a bullet had passed through him. Anton, who was so alive and warm and arrogantly maddening, had almost died, never to be known to her. It seemed incredible, astounding, that she might never have known him. It seemed impossible that by a hair's breadth they had almost never met.

'Look at me,' he ordered. 'I won't force you, *dorogaya*, I will merely ask you to stop staring at my chest and to look at my face instead. Come, I am being serious. I want you to look at the man who is going to tell you this minute that he loves you. That he has done so since the night he was trapped with you in a lift. Adorable *dorogaya*, for heaven's sake lift your face to mine before I go mad as only a Cossack can!'

She looked at him because she had to, because she desired to, but unbelievingly. He quirked an eyebrow in that inimitable way of his. 'You have heard of love, I take it?'

'But you don't believe in it,' she retorted.

'I thought not, but it seems that the heart has a will of its own. I could no more let you go after that night we were trapped together than I could let go my own life. Miroslava did not have to persuade me to follow you here. It was destined that I do so. You know it, too. It is there in your blue eyes. Rapture of the desert, *chérie*.'

'No——' She shook her head. 'I won't listen to you. I won't be swayed away from all that I've worked for, for the sake of an affair with a prince! I'm flattered——'

'You will be spanked in a moment, if you go on about affairs and careers, and all those boring things.' He pulled her so close to him that she lost her breath, and in his eyes looking down into hers there was such a heart-shaking look of love that she could hardly bear it.

'Don't do this to me,' she pleaded. 'It isn't fair! You're so accomplished in making a fool of a woman, and I—I don't know how to handle the situation.'

'Don't you?' He smiled down at her wickedly. 'You marry me, *dorogaya*, and you live with me a year in the desert, and if at the end of that time you still have this craving to dance, then——'

'You mean—you would allow me to dance?' She touched his face, almost shyly. Such a wonderful face ... it ought to be masked against all those women who would always look at him and desire the excitement of him.

'Of course,' he drawled. 'We will dance together at the Adonis Club. You remember how well your steps matched mine——'

'Oh, you devil!' Her fingers bent against his cheek, as if she would actually claw him, and then a smile slowly etched itself on her lips. 'I have a choice, it would seem. I can be your slave, or I can be a dancer. I wonder which I ought to choose. Both are taskmasters.'

'But only one will leave you lonely at night, and in the years ahead, Chrysdova, when the tawny hair loses its lustre and the sapphire eyes no longer sparkle—as they are sparkling right now.' He bent his head and he slowly and lingeringly kissed her lips. 'Will you deny me?'

'May I have time to think about it, Anton?' She pressed her cheek to the dark cross of hair on his chest, and felt at her fingertips the deep heartbeat, and the deep scar.

'Yes,' he agreed. 'You have exactly a minute.'

'Only a minute?' She smiled against him. 'How arrogant of you to expect me to give up a career in just one minute. It took me years to achieve it, and now I must sacrifice it for a man.'

She heard him laugh very softly. 'I promise that you won't regret your sacrifice, *dorogaya*. Think of all we shall share together. Desert rides and desert dawns. The sands whispering a thousand secrets when I hold you in my arms—as my bride. Come, little white-skinned devil, will you deny me?'

Chrys looked into those smoke-grey, wickedly beautiful eyes, and she thought of what Dove had said to her. 'For heaven's sake don't fall in love with the man!'

Chrys smiled and let her arms enchain his warm, brown neck. It was too late for warnings, too late for denials ... already she was giving herself to her desert prince.

Mills & Boon Classics

The very best of Mills & Boon
romances, brought back for those of
you who missed reading them
when they were first published.

There are three other Classics for you to collect this
May

A MAN APART
by Jane Donnelly

Everyone who knew Libby Mason hoped that she and Ian
Blaney would make a match of it, and they were all quick to
point out how misguided she would be to entertain any
romantic ideas about the 'outsider' Adam Roscoe. But wasn't
it just possible that 'everyone' might be wrong?

CHASE A GREEN SHADOW
by Anne Mather

Tamsyn had no doubt about her feelings for Hywel Benedict,
and it was equally clear that she affected him in some way —
but marriage? No, he said. He was too old for her. And there
were — other complications.

THE CRESCENT MOON
by Elizabeth Hunter

When Madeleine was stranded in Istanbul, there was no one to
whom she could turn for help except the lordly Maruk Bey,
who had told her that he found her 'dark, mysterious, and
very, very beautiful.' Could Madeleine trust such a man to aid
her?

If you have difficulty in obtaining any of these books through
your local paperback retailer, write to:

Mills & Boon Reader Service
P.O. Box, 236, Thornton Road, Croydon, Surrey, CR9 3RU.

Mills & Boon Classics

The very best of Mills & Boon
romances, brought back for those of
you who missed reading them
when they were first published.

In
June
we bring back the following four
great romantic titles.

ONE MAN'S HEART
by Mary Burchell
A harmless — well, fairly harmless — escapade took an
unexpected and horrifying turn that nearly landed Hilma in
serious trouble. But fortunately there was a handsome and
chivalrous stranger at hand to help her.

THE KISSES AND THE WINE
by Violet Winspear
Lise supposed she ought to be grateful to the imperious Conde
Leandro de Marcos Reyes for helping her out of an awkward
situation — but not so grateful that she was willing to repay
him as he suggested, by pretending to be his fiancée. A
domineering Spanish nobleman was not her idea of a comfortable husband. However, she reluctantly agreed to the
deception, just for a short time . . .

THE WATERFALLS OF THE MOON
by Anne Mather
'He's allergic to emotional entanglements,' Ruth declared after
she encountered the disturbing Patrick Hardy. But it was an
allergy that Ruth unfortunately didn't share and she tricked
Patrick into marriage and accompanied him to Venezuela.
Would her husband ever forgive the deception?

MAN IN CHARGE
by Lilian Peake
Juliet was delighted to get the job at Majors boutique, and full
of ideas and enthusiasm about it — but she found herself
continually in conflict with the man in charge, the chairman's
son, Drew Major. She wanted to keep the job — but was it
worth it, if it meant fighting this cynical man every step of
the way?

SAVE TIME, TROUBLE & MONEY!
By joining the exciting NEW...

Mills & Boon
Romance CLUB

WITH all these **EXCLUSIVE BENEFITS** for every member

NOTHING TO PAY! MEMBERSHIP IS FREE TO REGULAR READERS!

IMAGINE the *pleasure* and *security* of having ALL your favourite *Mills & Boon* romantic fiction delivered right to *your* home, absolutely POST FREE... straight off the press! No waiting! No more disappointments! All this PLUS all the latest news of *new books* and *top-selling authors* in your own monthly MAGAZINE... PLUS *regular* big CASH SAVINGS... PLUS lots of wonderful strictly-limited, *members-only* SPECIAL OFFERS! All these exclusive benefits can be *yours* — right NOW — simply by joining the exciting NEW *Mills & Boon* ROMANCE CLUB. Complete and post the coupon below for FREE full-colour leaflet. It costs nothing. HURRY!

No obligation to join unless you wish!

FREE CLUB MAGAZINE Packed with *advance news of latest titles and authors*

Exciting offers of **FREE BOOKS** For club members ONLY

Lots of fabulous **BARGAIN OFFERS** —many at **BIG CASH SAVINGS**

FREE FULL-COLOUR LEAFLET!

CUT OUT

CUT-OUT COUPON BELOW AND POST IT TODAY!

To: **MILLS & BOON READER SERVICE**, P.O. Box No 236, **Thornton Road, Croydon, Surrey CR9 3RU, England.** WITHOUT OBLIGATION to join, please send me FREE details of the exciting NEW Mills & Boon ROMANCE CLUB and of all the exclusive benefits of membership.

Please write in BLOCK LETTERS below

NAME (Mrs/Miss) ....

ADDRESS ....

CITY/TOWN ....

COUNTY/COUNTRY........................POST/ZIP CODE...........

S. African & Rhodesian readers write to:
P.O. Box 1872, Johannesburg, 2000. S. Africa